PROJECT MANAGEMENT

Complete Guide to Project Management

by

DENNIS LOCK

A CAHNERS MANAGEMENT GUIDEBOOK

Cahners Publishing Company, Inc
221 Columbus Avenue
Boston, Massachusetts 02116, USA
Telephone: Area Code 617-536-7780

Published in the United States by:

Cahners Publishing Company, Inc
221 Columbus Avenue
Boston, Massachusetts 02116
Telephone: 617-536-7780

Published in Great Britain by:

Gower Press Limited
13 Bloomsbury Square
London WC1
1969

Second Impression 1970

Library of Congress Card Number: 68-58694

A CAHNERS MANAGEMENT GUIDEBOOK

CONTENTS

1   PROJECT MANAGEMENT IN THE ORGANISATION   1
Some effects of growth on a small firm – Company
organisation and project organisation – Identifying the
project manager – Seniority of the project manager – The
project manager himself – Support and co-operation

2   DEFINING THE PROJECT   14
The customer's specification – The contractor's specification – Product specification

3   ESTIMATING THE COST AND FIXING THE PRICE   23
Listing the tasks – Breakdown of detail in project estimat-
ing – Task classification and coding – Estimating forms –
Production estimates – Collecting the estimates for labour
times – Material estimates – Interpreting the estimates –
Estimating characteristics of individuals – Contingencies –
Escalation – Fixing the price – Cost-plus projects –
Estimating accuracy

4   PLANNING THE TIMESCALE   48
Bar charts – Network analysis: an outline of CPA and
PERT – Shortening the timescale by rearranging the net-
work – Use of dummies to improve network clarity –
Standard networks – The networking session – Network
analysis as a basic tool

5   SCHEDULING RESOURCES AND PARTS   76
Case study: garage project – Activity float and resource
scheduling – Resource scheduling by computer – Schedules good and bad – Scheduling parts – Parts scheduling
by the line of balance technique

Contents

6   MATERIALS CONTROL   115
The purchasing cycle – Specifying the purchase order –
Ordering to a plan – The ABC system of stock control –
Purchase of small quantities – Expediting – Project
purchasing versus stock purchasing – Storage

7   MAINTAINING THE PROGRAMME   141
Making the project commitments known – Activity lists –
Departmental progress returns – The progress meeting –
Production priorities: immediate action orders – Haste
versus accuracy – Progress reports

8   MODIFICATIONS, BUILD SCHEDULES, AND CONCESSIONS   155
Origins of modifications – Estimating the true cost of a
modification – Recording the actual cost of a modification
– Authorisation of modifications – Emergency modifications – Build schedules – Concessions

9   RELATING ACHIEVEMENT TO EXPENDITURE   179
Design achievement – Regular achievement analysis –
Production achievement – Monitoring by milestones –
Materials achievement – Subcontract achievement – Effect
of modifications on achievement – The project ledger –
Predicting project profitability

INDEX   207

ILLUSTRATIONS

FIGURE		PAGE
1.1	Example of company organisation chart	5
1.2	The project cycle	7
3.1	Estimating levels	26
3.2	Estimating form	28
4.1	A simple project bar chart	50
4.2	The simplest network possible	53
4.3	Network restrictions	53
4.4	Tree project network	54
4.5	The critical path	55
4.6	Gantry project	56
4.7	Gantry project network: normal duration	58
4.8	Gantry project network: all activities crashed	60
4.9	Gantry project network: optimised crash action	61
4.10	Ladder networks	64
4.11	Using dummies to extend displayed information	66
4.12	Standard network	71–5
5.1	Garage construction network	78
5.2	Garage project resource schedule before levelling	80
5.3	Garage project resource histogram before levelling	81
5.4	Garage project resource schedule levelled	83
5.5	Garage project resource histogram with restrictions	84
5.6	Garage project resource schedule levelled	86
5.7	Garage project resource histogram levelled	87
5.8	Garage project float analysis	88
5.9	Garage project float analysis	89
5.10	Filing cabinet project	94
5.11	Simple parts list for filing cabinet	95
5.12	Filing cabinet family tree	97
5.13	Filing cabinet general assembly	98

List of Illustrations

5.14	Filing cabinet drawer assembly	99
5.15	Filing cabinet drawer chassis	100
5.16	Filing cabinet left side plate	101
5.17	Filing cabinet right side plate	102
5.18	Stock collation card	103
5.19	Stock collation card	104
5.20	Redrawn filing cabinet family tree	107
5.21	Calculation of lead times for filing cabinet parts	108
5.22	Filing cabinet delivery commitment	109
5.23	Line of balance for filing cabinet parts	110
5.24	Filing cabinet project	112
6.1	The purchasing cycle	118
6.2	The ABC method of stock control	126
6.3	Economic purchase quantity	129
6.4	Monitoring material costs	134
6.5	Shortage list form	139
7.1	Departmental activity list	143
7.2	Departmental progress return	145
8.1	Engineering change request form	162
8.2	A typical build schedule sheet	170
8.3	One type of concession request form	174
8.4	Engineering query note	175
8.5	Inspection report form	177
9.1	Typical departmental achievement analysis	185
9.2	Departmental achievement predictions	188
9.3	Costs compared to a simple prediction curve	191
9.4	Costs compared to project milestones	192
9.5	Progress ladders	200
9.6	Progress ladders in action	201
9.7	A cost/profit project prediction graph	204

1

PROJECT MANAGEMENT IN THE ORGANISATION

Project management is recognised as a specialised branch of management which has evolved in order to co-ordinate and control some of the complex activities of modern industry. It is, of course, not an isolated example of a management skill acquired through the necessity created by industrial development and expansion. Indeed the phenomenon of survival through specialisation is not new, and hardly originated in the world of industry and commerce.

One of the fundamental and most familiar aspects of everyday life is the growth of living things. This growth can be observed in a single plant, in a baby animal, or, more widely, in a whole colony or population. Sooner or later, development must depend upon the supply of natural resources in quantities sufficient to support the demands of the population. Competition for available food, water, and shelter must intensify as more mouths or roots require feeding. The effects of climate and predators add other elements of risk. In the course of time, only those organisms which are able to adapt themselves will manage to prosper. The rule of "survival of the fittest" will reign, resulting in the evolution of life forms which grow more and more specialised as time proceeds.

The world of industry suggests close parallels with the world of nature when the effects of growth and evolution are compared. Continuous expansion of firms within a generally expanding economy will create more demand for all the available resources. Evolutionary processes must occur as companies adapt themselves to meet the challenges presented by their continually changing economic climate. Some firms will emerge as more successful than others, whilst those which cannot readapt in time will be unable to survive at all.

Current trends in the greater use of electronic computers for data processing and machine control, the increase in size of many civil engineering projects, complex weapon systems for defence, and the establishment of better communication and transport links all require the participation of large contractors. Smaller firms either are unable to tender for large projects or must be content to accept a small slice of the cake as relatively unimportant subcontractors to their bigger brothers. Many small companies may in fact depend directly upon larger firms for their very existence.

Any firm which does not, for any reason, maintain a rate of growth which is at least in step with the current rate of industrial expansion will, in all probability, not merely stagnate but either fail altogether or be swallowed up by one of its more powerful rivals. Companies which remain too small may suffer from relatively high production costs, owing to the small volume of work which can be undertaken and the limited amount of capital available for investment in modern tooling, plant, and machinery. There will also be a restriction in the size of individual projects open to the smaller firm because the resources which it can muster will be limited.

SOME EFFECTS OF GROWTH ON A SMALL FIRM

The first assumption which can be made about any light engineering company is that if the firm is successful it must be expanding. This growth will be evident in many ways, including, for example, in increasing turnover and payroll, and also the occupation by the company of larger premises.

Suppose that this company employs a staff of about 100 people and is selling some sort of specialised apparatus or components. Manufacture would probably take place under the supervision of a production manager who would in turn rely upon a production control department to schedule all work. In normal conditions, the backlog of work awaiting issue to the shops at any given time might not run into more than a few weeks. Loading of production departments and their machines must be arranged to ensure effective usage and a smooth flow of work, but planning methods would be straightforward and within the capability of any competent production controller or his staff. If undue work peaks ever did occur, they could be overcome by rearranging existing schedules or by the short-term employment of subcontractors.

All drawings used for production will be vetted by production engineers and manufacturing times will be known both from estimates and actual experience. Manufacture could take place in small or large batches or as a continuous production flow. No need will be found for any specialised planning or scheduling technique other than the application of well-proven production control methods, such as daily loading bar charts. Job costing can be carried out in arrears, and since the time cycle from start to finish will be short for each operation, the cost of each unit produced will become known fairly soon.

However, this small company is expanding, and the sales department is going all out to get more orders. Not only will these orders increase in quantity, but it is also possible that some of them could call for non-standard items which do not form part of the customary production range. Many of these special items might be trivial variations on the normal production theme, but others could prove to be more complex, presenting something of a technical challenge.

In the course of time, the customers will themselves be expanding. Some of their orders will grow bigger not only in volume, but also in the timescale needed to fulfil them. Although these orders might consume large quantities of labour and materials, it is also possible that the actual quantity of finished products could be very few in number. They will have become so specialised that no possible market can be found for them outside the needs of the specific purchaser. This state of affairs is sometimes summed up as being a transition from high-volume–low-cost to low-volume–high-cost production.

To give a particular example, this imaginary company might once have been engaged in the manufacture of street lamps. Later, production could have been extended to include traffic signals, comprising a control box, vehicle-sensing pressure pads, and the signal lamps themselves. As traffic flow becomes more intense, traffic systems have to be planned on a much larger scale; the firm must increase its scale of operations accordingly. Instead of considering just an individual cross-roads or T-junction, whole town areas will have to be taken into account and subjected to analysis in order to arrive at a solution which integrates all requirements into a whole. When an order is finally placed for the town traffic system, the contractor could easily become involved in the supply and installation of much more than one set of traffic lights. He might find himself

3

caught up in the provision of automatic diversion signs, remotely controlled television cameras, car-parking instrumentation, and all sorts of other highly sophisticated paraphernalia.

No longer is the company concerned only with the sale of apparatus or "hardware" alone. They now have to support their sales with a high proportion of system engineering, customer consultation, and other services or "software." Instead of being able to satisfy each order by withdrawing finished articles from stock, the systems may have to be designed specially, and manufactured to specific customer requirements. Whereas delivery times were once achieved in a matter of a few weeks, modern complex projects might take many months, if not several years, to complete.

When the stage has been reached where simple jobs have given way to complex projects, the old methods of production planning and control will no longer be effective by themselves. Any attempt at work scheduling must take into account all activities necessary to bring the project to a successful conclusion, including the many software tasks. Control of profitability, from the estimating and pricing stage right through to budgetary control and final costing, cannot now be carried out by the cost office alone. They must be helped by experts who can define the detail of the total work content, and report on achievement as time proceeds. Possibly some of the items purchased outside the firm must be considered as special, and they too will have to be brought into the general control function.

COMPANY ORGANISATION AND PROJECT ORGANISATION

A clearer picture of some of the problems encountered in project handling can be derived from a study of the organisation structure of the company's supervision and management. One might expect to find that a small light engineering company is organised along the lines shown in Figure 1.1. Line organisations of this type are set up to control work within departmental boundaries. The chief engineer will be responsible for design and development and very little else, leaving the production manager to concentrate on production problems. Each manager is looking only at his own department and has no direct responsibilities outside. Of course, no company could ever exist solely upon such a rigid basis. Functional interplay between managers must take place. Nevertheless, any such functional

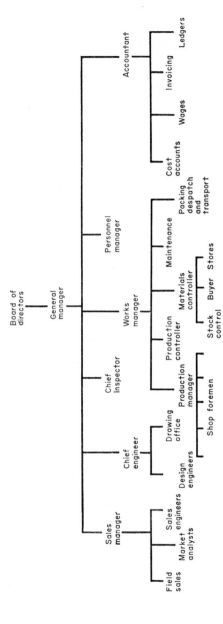

FIGURE 1.1 EXAMPLE OF COMPANY ORGANISATION CHART
This type of organisation defines line responsibilities but does not cater specifically for the co-ordination of project activities

5

relationships which do exist are seen as secondary to the main line structure. They are not brought under any sort of formal control.

One might reasonably ask whether the general manager should not play a significant part in co-ordinating all the various functions. The answer, of course, is that he does. His prime task, however, is to implement policies and carry out general administration, rather than to become involved with the day-to-day running of individual projects or technical detail. In the organisation structure depicted in Figure 1.1, there is in fact no one person who can logically be charged with the direct responsibility for following a major project right through all its stages. Whereas the line responsibilities are clearly defined and adequately manned, the co-ordination between them necessary for effective project control is missing.

It is possible to overcome many of the co-ordination problems characteristic of complex projects by establishing project groups. The design engineers, production facilities and many of the indirect services are formed into a project "task force," preferably placed under the command of one project leader. The life span of the group corresponds to the active duration of the project itself, so that the team is dispersed once the work has been finished.

Project groups have the advantage that they can be directed to one single purpose: the successful completion of one contract. They are completely autonomous and there is no clash of priorities resulting from a clamour of several different projects in competition for common production resources. If the project is for a government department and entails classification under the Official Secrets Act, the enclosure of all work and information within a group is obviously a security safeguard.

Unless the project is very large, however, the individual subgroups set up to perform activities within the project will prove to be too small to allow sufficient flexibility of labour and resources. Where, for example, a common production facility is coping with several projects, and has a total direct force of about 100 men, the absence of some workers because of sickness may demand some rescheduling but is unlikely to cause disaster. If, on the other hand, a project group has a production force of ten men, the infection of two of these with flu could prove a very serious problem indeed.

Inflexibility associated with small groups is perhaps felt most keenly in the indirect worker functions. Very often, only one man will be responsible for project purchasing or for project production control. It is not unknown for one man to be made responsible for both of these activities. When this situation is allowed to develop, the fate of the project may be dependent on the capabilities or health of just one individual, who becomes virtually indispensable. When inflexibility is introduced because of bad organisation, there is no capability to deal with sudden work peaks, however generated.

If a project is of sufficient size to justify its own exclusive group, not all the problems of project co-ordination will be overcome. Very often it will be found impossible to house all participants under one roof, or even in the same locality. The project leader could find that much of his time is devoted to sorting out technical problems or labour relations. Although the organisation may be logical, and ideal for the project, there might still exist a general lack of co-ordination between the different functions.

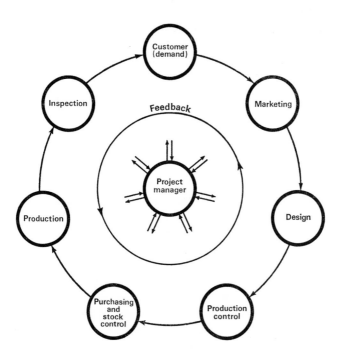

FIGURE 1.2 THE PROJECT CYCLE
A diagrammatic representation of the key stages in the progress of a typical project

All engineering projects, in common with most other customer funded projects, are cyclical in nature. This is illustrated in Figure 1.2. Each project is conceived when the customer makes his first contact with the sales department, and comes to life when an order is placed or a contract signed. Thereafter, many other interests must be involved in turn, until the project finally arrives back at the customer as a completed work package. Clockwise rotation around the cycle only reveals the main stream. Within this flow many small tributaries, cross currents, and even whirlpools will be generated before the project is finished.

As instructions are issued from one department to another, feedback information must be passed back along the communication channels to signal the results obtained when each instruction is carried out. This feedback data will be used to correct any errors arising from the design or in the execution of production work and to control the progress of the project generally. Much project information will flow not along the lines of authority but across them. In fact, the emphasis has shifted in the project situation from looking at the line relationships to consideration of the functional connections. At the hub of all project activities we see that a new figure has emerged. He is the project manager.

THE PROJECT MANAGER

Identifying the Project Manager. If any company were to be searched in order to discover the existence or otherwise of a project manager on the premises, the first results might be fruitless, since no one of that job title would be found. Usually the identity of the project manager is hidden behind some other organisational role. Even where project management is accredited the importance of a full-time appointment, the situation is made less clear by the variety of titles used to describe the job. Contract manager, scheduling and estimating manager, project co-ordination engineer, programme engineer, project co-ordinator are but a few of the total number of possible combinations. The job role itself would obviously be clarified if more companies agreed among themselves on a fairly standard job title. The most straightforward is project manager.

In any company which is caught up in industrial expansion, or in the so-called technological explosion, the project manager will be only one of the several specialised roles introduced. He can be numbered, for example, among the work study engineers, organisation and methods practitioners, computer programmers, systems analysts, and operational research men. He might have started his career in one of these activities, or he could be an engineer, commercial manager, or accountant. Not infrequently, the job of the project manager is associated with that of the contracts manager. This is a logical link because both will be expected to co-ordinate commercial and technical aspects of a company's work and both will occupy a position in the organisation which emphasises functional rather than line responsibilities.

Perhaps one of the more common routes to project management lies through the engineering design department. Frequently the engineer in command of a particular project is charged with a degree of overall responsibility for seeing the work right through to completion. When this situation develops, the engineer is doubling two roles, exercising a direct line supervision authority in controlling and guiding his engineering or drawing team whilst acting in a staff role when attempting to influence the other departments which are engaged on his project.

The project management function in a small company may be conducted entirely on a part-time basis by one of the existing departmental heads, or by some other individual as in the case of the engineer just described. Other companies may be forced to recognise the need for a full-time project manager appointment, the incumbent being held responsible for either one individual project or for several projects which are being handled simultaneously. Very large firms even have whole departments devoted to project management, where specialist teams operate as a central service.

Seniority of the Project Manager. The questions "how senior is the project manager?" and "to whom does he report?" now arise. A consideration of the general organisation, possibly helped by reference to Figures 1.1 and 1.2, may suggest a solution. The man appointed will 'ie expected to provide general management with any facts which are relevant to the need for executive action in maintaining the project on the financial, technical, and delivery course. He should therefore have reasonable access to general management. The job itself is largely one of co-ordination, combining and steering the activities of several departments. This demands co-operation with and from departmental managers, so that the co-ordinator himself should at least not be considered subordinate to any one departmental manager in particular or to all departmental managers in general.

The appointment level, therefore, appears to be indicated on a management plane which is at least equivalent to that occupied by departmental managers. This view becomes reinforced when it is realised that the man might be called upon from time to time to represent the company to subcontractors and (when the marketing phase is complete) to customers. He represents, in fact, part of the image which the company projects to the outside world.

The Project Manager Himself. It is hardly possible to lay down an ideal personality specification for a project manager. If the objectives of project management could be condensed into responsibility for ensuring work completion within time and cost restrictions, these objectives can be achieved by a wide variety of means. One man might find that he can induce fear and trepidation into his fellow men, so that his every word is taken as a command to be instantly obeyed. Another might achieve the same results through gentle but firm persuasion.

Some essential characteristics can be specified and most of these can be grouped under the heading of perceptiveness. The project manager must be able to select the salient facts from a set of data or a particular arrangement of circumstances. He must then be able to use these facts to best effect by reporting important exceptions to executive management whilst filtering out the unimportant and irrelevant material.

There is little doubt that the process of evolution of new project control techniques will continue. The project manager must be prepared to keep abreast of this development, undergoing training whenever necessary and passing on his training to other members of his firm when appropriate. He must be able to use these techniques directly, or adapted to suit his own purposes, whenever his project situation warrants. On the other hand, the temptation to impose unsuitable methods on an organisation, for the sole reason that they represent the height of current fashion, must be resisted. Here again, the correct course of action will be decided by the perceptiveness of the project manager.

Most project managers will be presented with information at some time in their project lives which is either misleading or completely wrong. Without going into the possible reasons for such inaccuracies, it is possible to lay down that a project manager must not be in any way a gullible individual. He will learn to check much of the information which he receives and he will know what questions to ask in order to probe the validity of statements given to him. As he gains experience of a particular organisation, he should be capable of assessing the reliability of individuals or departments, so that he can apply confidence factors to data which they submit.

The project manager, as a by-product of the technological era, could be described as a specialist. Certainly he will need to be given special training in one or more of the current management techniques if he is to operate effectively. Nevertheless, the term "specialist" can be misleading, since the major part of the project manager's work will be taken up with co-ordinating the activities of many varied project participants. This work will demand a wide understanding and knowledge of many different aspects of the company's administration without, necessarily, any particular degree of specialisation in one area.

If a man is asked to handle a flow of project data between different departments, he must be able to use his understanding of the company's administration to present the information in forms best suited to the individual needs of the various recipients. In computer terminology, the project manager may be asked to solve an interface problem, the solution to which demands some understanding of the operation of the peripheral equipment.

Support and Co-operation. No matter how experienced, competent, enthusiastic, and intelligent the man chosen for the job, he cannot expect to operate effectively without adequate support and co-operation. This support can be listed under several headings, which include support from higher management, acceptance and co-operation from all other key staff, the provision of essential facilities and equipment, the availability of suitable supporting clerical or other staff, and opportunities for further training as new techniques are developed.

If a man is engaged in the scheduling and progressing of work, it is inevitable that sooner or later he will be called upon to decide priorities or criticise progress in one or more departments. He must usually manage to issue any necessary instructions in the full knowledge that he has no direct authority over any one of the departments involved. Each departmental manager alone is responsible for the performance and day-to-day running of his own team. Any weight which the project manager's requests do carry must come as reflected authority from higher management, without whose ultimate backing the authority would be non-existent.

The main show of authority which the project manager can wield stems from his own personality and powers of persuasion. In these enlightened times, discipline no longer implies the imposition of rigid authoritarian regimes or the constant threat of punitive actions against offenders. Mutual co-operation is much more likely to prove an effective approach, especially in the long term. As a last resort, however, the full backing and support of higher management must be available as a reserve force on which the project manager can call in any hour of need.

Sometimes it would be apt to include project managers in that group of individuals described as "human dynamos." Certainly there will be times when apathy or inertia of some project participants has to be overcome by an electrifying injection of enthusiasm. The output of any dynamo, however, may be dissipated wastefully if it is switched into an inefficient or wrongly connected circuit. The project manager will learn to recognise any shortcomings in the organisation of his project forces. Whenever a change in the organisation is indicated, provided that the project manager can present a reasonable case, he should be able to rely on his management to make the appropriate administrative changes.

If the project manager is to be kept abreast of all new developments in project control, management must recognise that training is a continuous process and not simply a question of sending a man away for one two-day course on network analysis. In recent years there has been an increasing and welcome tendency for training authorities to arrange seminars where managers from different companies can meet to discuss mutual problems and exchange views. The effectiveness of the profession as a whole and of the individuals must benefit from this type of exchange.

Just as important as the training of the project manager is the creation of an enlightened attitude to scheduling and control methods by other project participants in the firm. The best way to achieve this ideal is to provide the project manager with the facilities to carry out a training programme of his own. He can then be allowed to explain his objectives and methods and give a basic grounding in networking techniques to all supervisors down to first line level.

Once the general objectives of project management have been appreciated by departmental managers and supervisors, their co-operation should be easier to obtain. If they understand the techniques, and especially the notation and language of network analysis, the co-operation, once obtained, will be far more effective. Higher management, after installing the project manager, must enable him to create an ideal environment in which to operate.

2

DEFINING THE PROJECT

Most projects originate within a company as a result of activity by the sales or marketing organisation, and engineering and production departments will therefore learn of most new project inquiries from this source. Discussions between the engineers and sales staff can be expected to arise from the need to prepare a tender to each prospective customer. If the company intends to make a serious bid for any project, the customer's requirements must first be clearly set out and understood.

THE CUSTOMER'S SPECIFICATION

Initial inquiries from customers can take many different forms. Perhaps a set of plans or drawings will be provided, or a written description of the project objectives. A combination of these two, rough sketches, or even a verbal request, are other possibilities. Ensuing communications between the customer and contractor, both written and verbal, may result in subsequent qualifications, changes, or additions to the original request. All of these factors, when taken together, constitute the "customer specification" to which all aspects of any tender must relate.

Should the quotation be successful and a firm order result, the contractor will have to ensure that the customer's specification is satisfied in every respect. His commitments will not only be confined to the technical details but will encompass the fulfilment of certain commercial conditions. The terms of the order may lay down specific rules governing methods for invoicing and certification of work done for payment. Inspection and quality standards may be spelled out in the contract and one would certainly expect to find a well-defined statement of delivery requirements. There may even be a condition which provides for penalties payable by the contractor should he default on the delivery dates laid down.

Any failure by the contractor to meet his contractual obligations could lead to loss of reputation and goodwill. He may become involved in actual financial loss if the programme cannot be met or if he has otherwise miscalculated the size of the task which he undertook. It is, therefore, extremely important for the contractor to determine in advance exactly what the customer expects for his money. He can then make certain that the progress of any project complies both technically and commercially with the terms of contract. This is a fundamental requirement for the control of any order and is part of the foundation on which successful project management must be built. If a project is not well defined from the outset, the attempts at control which follow can only be correspondingly loose and ineffective.

THE CONTRACTOR'S SPECIFICATION

Serious consideration of the customer's specification may lead to the preparation of a tender, in which case the contracting firm will have to put forward proposals for carrying out the work. These proposals will also provide a basis for the contractor's own provisional design specification. It is usually necessary to translate the requirements defined by the customer's specification into a form compatible with the contractor's own normal practice, quality standards, technical methods, and capabilities. The design specification will provide this link.

It should be observed here that the desired end results of most projects can be achieved by a variety of different methods; in any situation where several firms are competing for one order there will almost certainly be a considerable variation between the technical proposals put forward.

Taking a very simple example, suppose that there exists a requirement to position a lever by remote control. Any one of a large number of driving mechanisms could be chosen. Possibilities could include hydraulic, mechanical, pneumatic, or electromagnetic forces. Each of these methods could be subdivided into a further series of possible techniques. If, for example, an electro-magnetic system is chosen, it might be thought of in terms of a solenoid or a motor, driven by direct or alternating current. Options to use alternating current might call for single or multiphase, and voltage and frequency must also be selected. The motor or solenoid itself could be picked out from a very wide range and might have to be flameproof, or magnetically shielded, or be special in some other respect. Once the lever has been moved to a new position several ways of measuring the result for check purposes can be imagined. Optical, mechanical, electrical, or electronic techniques might be devised – or even a ruler could be used. Very probably the data obtained from the check would be used in some sort of control or feedback system to correct any small error. There would, in fact, exist a very large number of permutations between all the possible ways and means of providing drive, measurement, and feedback control. The arrangement eventually chosen might depend not so much on the optimum arrangement suggested by the particular situation as on the contractor's usual practice. The final selection could even be influenced by the personal preference of the design engineer assigned to the system study.

With the possibility of all these different methods for such a simple operation, the variety of choice may approach infinite proportions in the case of a major project. It is clear that coupled with all these different possibilities will be a corresponding range of different costs, since some methods, by their very nature, must always cost more than others. The price of a project, therefore, will not only depend on economic factors, such as the location of the firm and its cost/profit structure, but also on the technical proposals adopted.

Ways and means of estimating the costs of a project are considered in Chapter 3. It can already be seen, however, that owing to the possible variations in cost, the technical proposals must be established before serious attempts at estimating can start. Once the techniques have been decided they must be recorded in the provisional design specification. If this were not done, other more costly methods might be employed simply because the original intentions had been forgotten. This danger is very real and often occurs in practice, especially when the period between quotation and order extends to more than a few months. It has been known for a contract to stray so far from the original design concept that the cost estimates were overspent by more than 100 per cent.

A similar argument exists for the careful association of production techniques with production estimates. It may happen that certain rather bright individuals can come up with suggestions for cutting corners and saving money on predicted costs. Provided that these ideas are recorded with the estimates, all will be well and the cost savings achieved can be used to influence the price and profit forecasts. Now imagine the effect if, for instance, a project is taken on by one company in a large group and then passed to another member of the group for execution without any indication of the original production methods envisaged. The cost consequences could prove to be nothing short of disastrous. Unfortunately, it is not necessary to transfer work between locations for mistakes of this kind to arise. Even the resignation of one production engineer from the staff could produce these consequences. The golden rule, once again, is to define the project in all possible respects before the estimates are translated into budgets and price.

Construction projects offer another example of work which has to be defined by specification. The need to apply for planning permission from the local authority means that plans must be drawn up in any case before work can begin. There are, however, many detail aspects of a building project, including for instance, the style of interior decoration and the quality of fittings provided, which can greatly affect the cost. Disputes can be minimised, if not prevented altogether, by the contractor producing his own specification and asking the customer to accept it before the contract is signed. Any changes at the customer's request can then be charged as additions to the original order.

PRODUCT SPECIFICATION

Development programmes aimed at the introduction of additions or changes to a company's product range are perhaps more prone than most to the risk of overspending on both budgets and timescale. One possible cause of this phenomenon is that chronic engineer's disease which might be termed "creeping improvement sickness." Many will recognise the type of situation illustrated in the following example.

Imagine that a company producing record players for domestic users has carried out a market survey operation. From the results of this study they plan to introduce a new model, aiming at a gap in the market where competition is forecast to be lowest and where a good demand either exists or can be created by sales promotion. The model which is wanted will be in the medium price range and, although not exactly in the "hi-fi" category, it must be capable of good performance without obvious distortion. The image to be created is that of good quality at a reasonable price.

We can visualise the launching of the new design, starting with a meeting in the chief engineer's office in the company's development laboratories. In addition to the chief engineer, the meeting would probably contain representatives from other interested departments, including sales and production. The other member needed to establish the necessary quorum is, of course, the design engineer appointed to carry out the actual development work.

The discussion would undoubtedly be aimed at setting the engineer off along the right track to create the unit envisaged by the company's directors on the basis of the market survey. Thus the engineer (George) will be provided with a set of objectives. Let us assume, however, as often happens, that these objectives are fairly broadly based and not written into a formal specification. Suppose, therefore, that George emerges from the meeting with mental notes of a verbal briefing, plus possibly his own rough notes and sketches. He will have been given some idea of target production costs, the associated selling price, styling, performance, and an approximate date for market release. By any standards this can be regarded as a small project, requiring some degree of programme control but not demanding any sophisticated project management techniques.

We can safely assume that George will be fairly bubbling over with enthusiasm. Most engineers become keen when suddenly given responsibility for a new project on which their creative abilities can be unleashed. After a few weeks of active work behind the closed doors of his laboratory, George can be expected to emerge with the first experimental model of the new record player. This working model must then be subjected to the critical attention of various experts, among whom may be production engineers, an industrial designer, and marketing staff.

Following successful evaluation of the prototype, the next stage in the project will be to prepare a set of production drawings from which a pilot production batch can be manufactured. Other associated work could include preparation of a provisional series of publica-

18

tions, such as maintenance and servicing instructions and sales leaflets. One might reasonably expect, from experience, that this pre-production phase of a project would take considerably longer than the original design of the laboratory model. We can imagine, therefore, that a period of waiting must be tolerated whilst the drawing office produces layouts, works out manufacturing tolerances, prepares and checks parts lists, and so on.

In the meantime, however, George has been having second thoughts. He has realised that he could have cheapened the amplifier circuit by the use of lower grade components, without sacrificing performance. This incidentally requires a redesign of the printed circuit wiring, at a stage when the printed circuit boards have been drawn, and ordered in prototype quantities. George feeds the new information through into the drawing office and cancels the outstanding order for prototype boards. The drawing office, in turn, advise production of the hold-up and carry out the necessary redesign. While the drawing office have been busily engaged in updating their drawings and reissuing the provisional parts lists to the purchasing department, the estimators have been at work. They have discovered that the saving achieved by using lower grade components amounts to only 1 per cent of the total production cost. So far, the change has caused a three-week hold-up in the programme.

George, impatient that the new drawings seem to be taking so long, has had very little with which to occupy his active mind. He suddenly comes up with the idea that he could have used a different loudspeaker. A new model, just introduced on to the market has a frequency characteristic which is so well suited to the proposed cabinet design that the bass response can be extended downwards by a whole octave. Unfortunately, the increase in size of the replacement loudspeaker will result in further drawing modifications and scrappage of some of the work already carried out on the pilot batch. George considers that this is a small price to pay for the significant increase in performance which can be expected and decides to go ahead and introduce the change.

At length, and in spite of all the delays, the prototype batch is completed and passed over to the laboratory for testing and evaluation. George is dismayed to find that every single one of the new models exhibits two faults which were not present on the first experimental unit. Apart from distortion at low frequencies, there is also an intrusive amount of hum and rumble. Examination reveals that the distortion was really introduced when the lower grade circuit components were used. The trouble was not noticed before simply because the original loudspeaker did not reproduce the troublesome frequencies. The appearance of mains hum and turntable rumble can be attributed to the same cause – the improvement of the low frequency response.

Three possible choices are now open to George. He could revert to the design of the first laboratory model, using the original loudspeaker. George, however, has high ideals and the idea of degrading the performance does not appeal to him. He could introduce filter circuits to cut the bass performance so that the noise becomes attenuated, but this again would be a degrading of the performance. George therefore decides to do the only proper thing. He modifies the rectifier circuit to remove the mains hum and fits an improved turntable to cure the rumble. These changes call for an increase in production costs and use up more drawing office time. The eventual result, however, is outstandingly good and the standard of performance of the completed prototype measures up to George's most critical requirements. George is well pleased with the results of his efforts and congratulates himself on a job well done.

The management may not be so well pleased. The new model has been produced several months later than the original target date and the production cost per unit has become so high that it will not be possible to retail the unit economically at the intended price. In any case, the gap in the market where the demand originally lay has since been filled by a competitor's product and this would not have happened if the unit had been produced at the right time. George has, in fact, designed a good unit but not the product which he was asked to design. He has allowed his own ideas to intrude and he has lost sight of the original intentions. He has allowed the "best" to become the enemy of the "good."

This simple example serves to show some of the pitfalls which can arise from uncontrolled product development, without an adequate project specification. One can also see that the development costs will have exceeded budgets. The well-worn phrase "time is money" is as true in project management as anywhere, and it is usually fairly safe to assume that if a planned timescale has been exceeded the budget will also have been overspent (*see* Chapter 9).

It might be as well to take a second look at this imaginary project and see how the course of events would have run under a regime which employed some of the rudiments of project control. The first noticeable difference would have been the provision of a product specification to ensure that all the objectives were clearly defined from the start. One should expect to find an account of the performance, styling, weight limit, price target, and maximum permissible production costs. The cost and price data must always be related to the quantities produced so that a sales forecast should be included in the specification covering at least three years ahead.

In order to calculate the expected return on capital investment from sales of these products, the management must start with a fair idea of what this investment will be. Budgets for tooling costs and for development expenditure should therefore be decided upon at the beginning and these decisions will also have to be set down in the product specification. Finally there is the question of timescale. The target date for market release must be chosen carefully in advance as being an objective which can, in fact, be achieved. Quite often the date chosen will allow announcement of the new model at an annual national trade exhibition.

Now suppose that George has reached the stage where previously he was allowed to introduce his first circuit design change. Under conditions of effective control he would not be able to instruct the drawing office to alter their work unless he had first obtained permission from the other departments likely to be affected. It is usual for changes of this nature to be brought up for approval before a "change committee." They will assess all the possible effects of any proposed change on stocks and work-in-progress, reliability, timescale, and so on before giving their consent. In our example we may be certain that the adverse effects on timescale would have been weighed against the marginal savings in production costs, and the change would have been rejected.

The detailed consideration of modification control is presented in Chapter 8. It is enough at this stage to note that the other modifications which were introduced in the record player project would also have met with an early demise under a sound administration. George would have been kept along the right lines by the provision of a formal product specification and development programme, by the sensible control of modifications, and, of course, by the day-to-day supervision of his superiors.

A more effective timescale control could have been provided simply by preparing a bar chart, on which all the important events or "project milestones" were depicted. Even a simple chart of this type can be used to good effect in ensuring that regular checks on progress are maintained.

3

ESTIMATING THE COST AND FIXING THE PRICE

An accurate estimate of project costs provides a proper basis for management control. Before any worth-while attempt at cost estimating can even be considered, it will be necessary to write down a list of all the individual project tasks. The objective here must be to establish the most logical breakdown of all the jobs which can be foreseen, avoiding any omissions if possible. One could not reasonably expect a project manager, or indeed any other person to attempt this listing entirely on his own. One ought to picture a discussion session taking place between specialists from the relevant production and design departments. By involving these experts, all probable features of the project can be examined and a sensible work plan evolved.

LISTING THE TASKS

The most convenient occasion on which to produce the task list would be that set aside for the preparation of detailed timescale charts or delivery schedules. Construction of a critical path network at this time often brings activities to light which might otherwise have been overlooked. This in itself can repay the effort expended in drawing up an arrow diagram, even without regard to the degree of control which it will afford later on in the programme.

If the work to be carried out includes any hardware identical to that supplied against previous orders, it may be possible to find or draw a detailed "family tree" or "goes-into chart." Usually, however, these most useful documents will just not be available, since at this early stage in the project no production drawings will exist from which to derive them.

23

The task list must include not only all obvious items of project hardware, but also every associated software job. "Software" is a term fairly familiar in the project sense, thanks to the advent of the computer. We should realise, however, that projects quite remote from computer work can create a software demand. Schedules for production inspection and testing, and maintenance and instruction manuals may have to be specially written. These, together with any other documentation specified in the contract, should be regarded as tasks which must be included in the estimated costs.

Activities often forgotten during the estimating phase, only to be remembered too late for inclusion in the project price, include incidental production processes such as paint spraying, inspection, and testing. In some firms these may be covered by the general overhead rate, but in many others they will not, and must be numbered among the direct cost estimates. Protective plating, silk screen printing, engraving and so on are frequently omitted from estimating schedules. A more serious victim of neglect sometimes encountered is the work entailed in final commissioning and customer acceptance of the completed project.

Some very complex contracts demand that the contractor provides training facilities for some of the customer's technicians. Training sessions can involve senior engineers in much hard work, both in actual lecturing and in preparing their material beforehand. Incidental expenses may also arise from the provision of meals and accommodation for the trainees.

In fact, any task which is inadvertently left out of the task list during the estimating period will result in an underestimate for the project as a whole. This in turn could jeopardise any attempt at timescale planning and resource scheduling. Worse still, the extra work will have to be paid for, not out of budget, but from profits.

BREAKDOWN OF DETAIL IN PROJECT ESTIMATING

Some difficulty may be experienced in deciding how much detail to show in the task list. What is a "task" for this purpose? In the absence of any production drawings it would obviously not be possible to list all the manufacturing operations necessary to produce each separate piece part. It will not even be known how many piece parts are going to be needed for the project at this early stage.

Project estimates are therefore carried out on a broader scale than run-of-the-mill production estimates.

Ideally, each task should be selected so that it is small enough to be visualised as a complete entity for estimating purposes. On the other hand, the size of a task must be large enough to represent a measureable part of the whole project. The design and manufacture of each subassembly from a main piece of equipment might rank for consideration as a task, whilst the final assembly of all these sub-assemblies into one whole main assembly could be regarded as another. Writing, editing, and printing an instruction manual is another piece of work worthy of inclusion in the task list. Every one of these examples illustrate a specific part of the project, not only to make the job of estimating easier, but also, as will be seen later, to provide measureable units of achievement.

TASK CLASSIFICATION AND CODING

Reference to Figure 3.1 will help to clarify the foregoing arguments and illustrate the difference in scale between project estimating and production estimating. Six estimating levels are shown, ranging from the total project right down to individual manufacturing operations. The "activity" level corresponds approximately to the activities of the network diagram. This is the lowest level which is likely to occur in project estimating. The wealth of detail in the bottom two layers, greatly simplified in this example, cannot be defined until all the production drawings have been completed, much later on in the project programme.

In the example chosen, the tasks fall naturally into four main groups. Most projects can be split up similarly into logical main parts, and it is useful to group the task list into corresponding sections. This allows a concentration of control effort on to each portion. If the contract is very large, control could be delegated so that one or more task groups would be allocated to each individual of a project management team.

Code numbers can be provided to identify each group, task, and activity. Notice that in the example given in Figure 3.1 it is possible to recognise the relationship between associated tasks and activities from the build-up of these code numbers. All tasks in group 200 for example have codes starting with the digit 2. All activities required

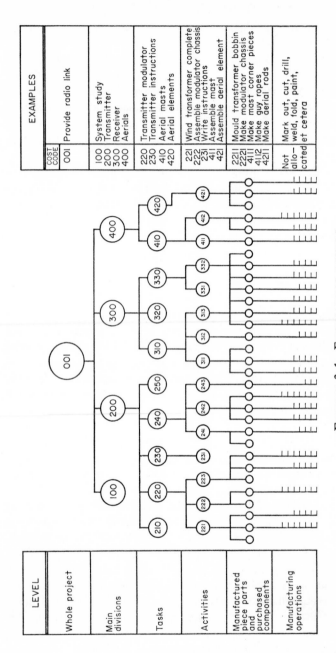

FIGURE 3.1 ESTIMATING LEVELS

This chart demonstrates different levels of detail at which project estimates can be considered

26

to complete task 240 start with the digits 24. Provided that the relevant departments are consulted, it is often possible to devise a comprehensive numbering system which can tie-in with the firm's cost code and drawing number arrangements. Certainly the cost code aspect should be taken up if at all possible, but the drawing numbers may prove a little too difficult. If one comprehensive scheme can be set up, much cross-referencing will be saved later on and there will be a substantial reduction in the possibility of clerical errors.

ESTIMATING FORMS

Completion of a detailed task list has established a basis from which project estimates can be made. When the estimates are collected, a large number of figures will be assembled. These should preferably be written down in some sort of tabular arrangement to allow easy reference, detailed analysis, and extension into totals – both for departments and task groups. A certain amount of discipline has to be imposed on the estimating function in order to ensure that procedures are reasonably standardised throughout a company, and from one project to another. By the accrual of project estimates carried out according to a standard procedure, results can be compared between different projects, and estimating made gradually more and more accurate as the experience is built up.

Some contracts, especially those for HM Government, may become liable to cost investigation from Technical Cost Officers at one or more stages. Careful attention to detail in presenting the estimates, and setting them out in an orderly fashion can create the best sort of impression right from the start. In all probability, the investigations will be exhaustive and taken into considerable detail. Starting off on the right foot will help to establish the good relations between customer and contractor which will be found essential in fixing a fair price.

Observance of company policy on cost rates and costing methods, as well as the necessity to determine project working budgets, all impose an obligation on the project manager to ensure that the estimates are set down in a standard and logical manner. Calculations performed in odd corners of notebooks, on scraps of paper, and on the backs (or fronts) of envelopes are prone to the possibility of error or premature loss. They will be unlikely to fulfil any of the other

FIGURE 3.2 ESTIMATING FORM
One type of form which can be used for most light
engineering projects. Similar forms can be adapted for a
wide variety of projects by choosing suitable column
headings

ESTIMATE FOR _____ SALES REF _____ SERIAL NUMBER _____
WORKS ORDER NUMBER (IF KNOWN) _____ SHEET ___ OF ___ SHEETS
COMPILED BY _____ DATE _____

1	2	3	LABOUR									MATERIALS			15
COST CODE	ITEM	QTY	DESIGN		PRODUCTION				10	11	12	13	14	FACTORY COST
			4	5	6	7	8	9	TOTAL WAGES £	OVER-HEADS £	DIRECT COST £	OVER-HEADS £	LONGEST LEAD TIME	10+11 +12+13
			ENGINEER	DRAW	SHEET METAL & M/C SHOP	FEMALE ASSEMBLY	MALE ASSEMBLY	TEST						
			HRS £	HRS £	HRS £	HRS £	HRS £	HRS £						

conditions already mentioned. In other words, an estimating form is needed.

One type of estimating form is illustrated in Figure 3.2. This particular example is in use for projects ranging in value from less than £1000 to over £500 000. The type of work covered includes complex electronic systems, steam steriliser equipment for hospitals, prefabricated steel building structures, and other parts associated with these products. In fact, this format is suitable for any light engineering undertaking although firms might need to adapt the arrangement of columns to suit their own particular accounting system.

Project estimating forms can be arranged to fit in with the estimating levels defined by Figure 3.1. One sheet could be allocated to each main project division, or task group, whilst every row on the forms would be occupied by one task. Each column entry denotes an activity. Adding each row yields the cost for the relevant task, which is very convenient for pricing spare parts. Adding the columns gives the estimated commitment expected for each department engaged on the project, and the result is used for resource scheduling and department budgeting.

Many attempts at the design of estimating forms fail because they are over-ambitious. There is no need to provide a column for every possible contingency. Instead, one or more columns can be left with the headings blank, so that these can be filled in as required later for special activities. Special tooling does not require individual treatment on the form as it will be treated as an ordinary task every time it crops up and can be written in along rows in exactly the same way as all other tasks.

Wage rates and overhead percentages have been omitted from the column headings, since these are semi-variables which change from time to time and must always be applied at the levels current at the time of estimating. For the same reason, the basic labour estimates should be entered in man-time and afterwards converted to money. We can generally take it that whilst wage rates will change from year to year, the times required to carry out any particular job by a given method will not. Man-time is therefore a fundamental basis for all estimates, whilst the conversion to money can only be regarded as a derivative, dependent on other variable factors.

In the materials section there are two columns in addition to that obviously needed for the direct cost of each task. Overheads can be applied to material purchases in order to recover the costs of preparing purchase orders, and of administering material control generally. Many firms, however, do not allocate overheads in this way, preferring to recover their material administration expenses together with the general labour overheads. Column 13, therefore, may not find universal application.

The column headed "longest lead time" is not connected in any direct sense with cost estimating, but is a very useful inclusion for the purposes of timescale prediction. Estimates will have to be made of delivery times for all the purchased items required for each task. Whichever procurement or "lead" time is longest for any particular task must determine the lead time for the procurement of all materials for that task.

If these longest lead-time estimates can be entered on to the estimating forms, the usefulness of each set of sheets is immediately extended, enabling them to be used as a source of information for timescale planning. All the timescale estimates on the network diagram, bar chart, or any other planning schedule can now be derived from one set of documents. Lead times, unlike cost estimates, are expressed in "elapsed time" and not in "man-time" units, since they do not represent any measure of work.

Additional columns could be provided on the estimating form to allow mark-ups and selling prices to be shown. These have been omitted from our particular example deliberately, in order to stress the fact that relationships between cost estimates and selling prices are sometimes too complex to allow calculation on a simple form. More will be said about project pricing later in this chapter.

PRODUCTION ESTIMATES

Estimates with Production Drawings. Suppose that an estimate is to be prepared for the routine production of a box from sheet metal. A set of manufacturing drawings is needed first. Other important factors likely to influence the answer would be the total quantity required and the rate at which they were to be produced. Further necessary information would include the type of production facilities which could be deployed and the amount of money to be spent on tooling.

All these facts would allow each drawing to be split up into a series of production elements, or operations. Every single step necessary to convert the raw material into a finished box could be listed in great detail, and in chronological order, on to a schedule or "process sheet."

An estimate of the labour time required for every individual operation, whether for cutting, folding, punching, welding, riveting or whatever, could be found by reference to data accumulated from past experience. In fact, tables of standard times for all routine operations would almost certainly be available. The degree of detail achieved in some sets of standard time tables is very comprehensive. If, for instance, it is required to find how long a particular hole would take to drill, the material thickness, the hole diameter, and the material itself are all variables which might be taken into account, so that the exact part of the table could be referred to for those specific needs. Welding could be estimated in man-seconds per inch of weld. Times for jigging or machine set-up might also be well documented.

In a very large-scale mass production, estimating and work measurement can reach a pitch where the times for operator limb movements are considered, these being measured in man-seconds or even finer units of time. Each operation itself is then "synthesised" from all the tiny constituents which it contains. Estimating at this level of detail is not shown in Figure 3.1. If it were to be included on the diagram, a separate space would have to be provided immediately below the "operation" level and labelled "synthetics." Routine production times can often be predicted with such accuracy that the answers are given in man-minutes. In the case of our metal box, we could probably finish up with a very good estimate, obtained by adding together all operation times, factored to allow for a known proportion of non-productive time – for example, tea breaks, clocking on and off, and so on.

If each box had to contain some sort of apparatus or instrumentation, the assembly time could also be forecast from standard times with a fair degree of accuracy. The number of screws or rivets to be used, the size, length, and number of wires and pipes, and the types of connections could all be counted up from the drawings. Once again, the estimates would be read off as production times for each operation from standard tables, derived from the known characteristics and performance of the organisation and its operators.

It is possible to forecast materials expenditure with ease and certainty for production work. Raw material usage can be assessed by examination of drawings, and making allowances for cutting wastage, breakages, and losses. Other materials are listed in advance by the drawing office on the bills of material or parts lists, and it is only necessary to pass these over to the purchasing department or cost office to have the standard costs filled in.

This brief account of routine production estimating has little or nothing to do with the subject of project management, except to serve as a contrast against which particular difficulties can be discussed. Notice that several key factors can be isolated from the routine methods. Work is always broken down into small elements before estimates are applied. The estimates themselves can usually be described as either "standard" or "known" quantities, and any possibility of guesswork is eliminated. Reliance is placed not on personal opinions of how long each job should take, but on the results of long experience and scientific work measurement.

Estimates Without Production Drawings. Suppose now that an estimate is to be prepared for the manufacture of a box filled with instrumentation, but that this time no production drawings have been prepared. Only one box is to be made, since it will be required for a special project. The only description on which the estimates can be based is an artist's sketch, showing the exterior of the box, and an engineer's written design specification which includes no detail at all of dimensions, materials, or the contents of the box, other than to outline the functional performance of the completed product.

Standard estimating tables are not likely to be of any help at all in this kind of situation. Build-up of standards depends upon the establishment of production continuity which demands in turn that a certain minimum volume of production must take place. Such standards cannot be applied to "one-off" production, where the unknown variables take over to dominate the picture. In any case, there are no drawings from which to break the work down into operations, and so the standards – even if they were valid – could not be applied.

A stage in the project planning process has now been reached where many professional estimators, production engineers, and work study devotees find themselves foundering well out of their normal depth. Their trusted books of standard times, with which they have worked for many years, and much of their professional training will become virtually useless when they are faced with the problem of estimating for work where no drawings exist. They have learned to regard drawings as their customary means of expression and communication. Without such aids they are rendered helpless. They feel deprived and are quite unwilling to commit themselves to giving forecasts which may require justification later.

The problem of project estimating is not made any easier by the short space of time usually available. All too often a tender has to be prepared within a few days in order to meet a deadline set by the prospective customer. Failure to meet the closing date could mean that the order is automatically lost to a competitor. Within these few available days, of course, an estimate would be required not just for one box like the one in the example. There may be hundreds of such boxes, all different, and all to be manufactured singly. Even if drawings could be found there would not be sufficient time in which to analyse them. Estimating itself costs money and it is possible to spend too much time predicting project expenditure, especially where no deadline has been fixed. Probability of obtaining the order may be too low to justify much expenditure on preparation of a tender.

There is no simple solution to all these problems, but it is possible to outline a new line of approach which is more likely to yield results. Fortunately the lack of drawings, and the necessity for making estimates in a short space of time, are two conditions which demand a similar handling technique. Project estimating, as has already been seen, is carried out on a much broader scale than run-of-the-mill production work. Larger work packages must be visualised. With the broader view, the level of seniority of the estimator rises, until the production manager himself could become involved.

With the small example of a metal box filled with instrumentation, the estimating method might proceed along the following lines. First, a description of the proposed box would be needed, with some idea of its contents. The engineers must provide this information since they are the only people at this stage who can possibly have any real idea what the final, detailed, article will be like.

Once a description of the new box has been set down it is usually possible to find a previous piece of work which bears some resemblance to the new job. Once again, the engineers are the only people who can be asked to make such comparisons at this stage. It might be said that no direct parallel exists but that one previous job was carried out which was somewhat simpler than the present object of concern. "How much simpler?" is the question which must now be asked. The engineer may say that about 10 per cent more components will be needed this time, giving a basis on which to approach the production department for an estimate.

When the records of expenditure on a previous box have been looked up and these facts given to the production foreman or production manager, an estimate for the new work can be reasonably requested, provided the fact is explained that about 10 per cent more components will have to be assembled. If the old box took one man-week to fabricate, this may be considered a good enough estimate for the new one. Only a couple more holes are going to be needed to fix the extra components. Wiring and piping must take longer, however, since there will be 10 per cent more components, and therefore a corresponding increase in the number of connections which must be made. A previous assembly time of two man-weeks might therefore be extended to an estimate of two and a half man-weeks for the more complex box.

Such estimates should not be expressed in terms of man-minutes. Using fine units of time exposes the estimator to the same trap as the scientist who carries out an experiment using measurement accuracies to three significant figures and then expresses his final result to four significant figures, simply because he used four-figure logarithms. The last two figures of his answer cannot be justified. Neither can any talk of man-minutes in production estimates without drawings.

Familarity with the idea of regarding production times on broad project scales means that they can be collected in exactly the same way as estimates for engineering, drawing, and other non-productive activities. The estimating system can therefore be standardised and all cost predictions collected according to one set of rules.

COLLECTING THE ESTIMATES FOR LABOUR TIMES

Ideally, project estimates should always be sought from those departments best qualified to provide them. In this type of work there is a shift of emphasis compared to routine production estimating. With the latter, responsibility for forecasting costs can safely be vested in one department or individual, whose sole task is either estimating or production engineering. Project estimates, on the other hand, must usually be obtained from senior departmental individuals who are going to be responsible for carrying out the actual project duties later. It would be reasonable for example, to expect the chief engineer to provide all the engineering design estimates, the chief draughtsman to give those for drawing, and so on. The production manager, purchasing manager, and some shop foremen might also become involved.

Decentralising the estimating function in this way reflects the change in scale when progressing from production estimating to project work. It is not done simply to produce more accurate estimates, although that should always be the chief aim. When a large project is being planned, the cost forecasts can have a profound influence on the manning and budgets of the affected departments for some time to come. Any departmental budget, whatever the type of work involved, can only be effective if the departmental manager has played a major part in agreeing his budget targets. In the case of a big project, this means that he must produce, or at least agree, the estimates.

If the estimating function is to be decentralised, it follows that the set of project estimating forms must be circulated among all the participating departments. This can be done in several ways with varying degrees of effectiveness. One master set of forms could be assembled, attached to a circulation list, and sent to the first-named department on the list. Each department would be expected to pass on the forms to the next, until all the estimates having been completed the bundle would arrive back on the project manager's desk. Everyone knows how long a library copy of a magazine takes to complete its circulation, if indeed it ever does return to the library. This method can therefore be dismissed as impracticable, owing to the inevitable and intolerable delays which would result.

A second possibility is to run off a set of pre-headed estimating forms for each department, and send them all out simultaneously. This has the advantage of cutting out the serial delays of the first suggestion but still relies on the whole-hearted co-operation of all the departmental heads. Late returns can still be expected, while it is known from bitter experience that some sets may even be lost altogether. It is an indisputable fact that estimating is regarded as an unpleasant task, to be avoided at all costs if any other priorities can be found as excuses. Therefore no one can expect to rely solely upon written requests for forms to be filled in. A more direct approach appears to be necessary.

Another way in which to collect all the estimates would be to ask for them in detail during the network analysis session (described in detail in the next chapter). This occasion provides the opportunity, since all the key project members could be expected to be on hand. The real snag here is that by the time the network has been drawn, several hours will have elapsed, and protracted meetings do not produce the best results. In fact, the law of diminishing returns starts to apply whenever any meeting exceeds about two hours in duration. Most members will start to feel drowsy, or fidget, or want to get back to their departments to sort out some problem which is undermining their peace of mind. However, for some simple projects, provided the meeting does not become too extended, the estimates can be written straight on to the network drawing and copied off on to the estimate forms afterwards. Material costs would, of course, have to be carried out as an additional exercise, since the network will normally only be concerned with time, unless some sophisticated PERT/cost set-up is to be used.

Short of applying legal compulsion, or threat of physical violence, personal canvassing by the project manager is the method most likely to provide quick and dependable results. The technique demands that the project manager arms himself with a set of estimating forms on which all the tasks and codes have already been listed. He can then embark on a tour of all the departments involved, installing himself purposefully at each manager's desk in turn. The aim is to remain firmly rooted to every department until all the desired data has been extracted. The project manager may make himself a little unpopular in the process, but it is not part of any project manager's job to become well liked.

Canvassing for estimates affords the project manager an opportunity to assess the estimating capabilities of all the individuals whom he meets. Any figure which appears unrealistic or outrageous can be questioned on the spot, and many other details can be sorted out with the least possible fuss. One type of question which must frequently be asked of the estimator takes the form: "Here is a job of four man-weeks; can four men do it in one week, or must it be carried out by only one man, taking four weeks of elapsed time?" The answers are of obvious importance in resource scheduling, of which more will be said later on.

Production staff often need help in their estimating task, and the project manager can often supply this during his tour. He can assist by translating the design specification into terms which the production people can understand, although he must be careful not to read anything into the specification which is not there. Similarities with past projects can be suggested and any artists' impressions or other sketches which may be available can be amplified by verbal description. Any real doubts which arise over the specification must, however, be referred back to the engineer in charge, since the project manager is expected to co-ordinate and not interfere with design.

MATERIAL ESTIMATES

Materials always require two types of estimate. These are the total expected cost for each task, and the time required to obtain the longest delivery item to complete each task. Both of these estimates are usually vital to project control work. Material costs often account for more than half the total cost of a project whilst the failure to obtain materials on time is possibly the most frequent cause of programme slippage.

If design has yet to be carried out, we know that we shall not have the benefit of parts lists or bills of materials on which to base our estimates. Therefore we must do the next best thing and ask the engineers to prepare provisional lists of materials for each task. This may be almost impossible to carry out in any detail but not so difficult as it would first seem. In most work, one usually has a very good idea of the major items which will have to be purchased. These may be special components, instruments, or control gear. In other cases there could be a certain requirement for large deliveries of raw materials or construction materials. Items such as these can account for a significant proportion of the costs and are frequently those which will take longest to obtain.

Foreknowledge of the major items of expense enables a reduction of the unknown area of estimating and improves the accuracy of forecasting. If all the important items can be listed and priced, the remaining miscellaneous purchases can be guessed. Records of past projects can be consulted to help assess the probable magnitude of the unknown element. If, for example, the known major components are going to account for 50 per cent of the total material costs, and an error of 10 per cent is made in assessing the remainder, there is an overall mistake in material expenditure of only 5 per cent. It is very important, however, to prepare a careful list of all the known items, and to make certain that the job is done conscientiously, so that none are forgotten.

The purchasing department should always be involved in materials estimating, and all prices and delivery times must be obtained through their efforts whenever possible. If they are not allowed to partake in the preparation of the detailed estimates, there exists a real danger that when the time comes to order the goods they will be obtained from the wrong suppliers at the wrong prices. It is far better if the big items of expense can be priced by quotation from the suppliers. The buyer can file all the quotations away in readiness for the time when the project becomes live. If the purchasing department is to be held down to a materials budget for any project, then it is only reasonable that they should play the major role in producing the material estimates.

Materials estimating, therefore, places responsibility in two areas. The engineers or design representatives must specify what materials are going to be used, and the purchasing department will be expected to say how much they will cost, and how long they will take to obtain.

Interpreting the Estimates

When all the estimates have been entered on to the estimating forms, it should, theoretically, be possible to add them all up and pronounce a forecast of the whole project costs. When this stage has been reached, however, it is never a bad plan to stand well back for a while, and view the picture from a wider angle. In particular, try converting the figures for labour times into man-years, taking 2000 man-hours as being roughly equal to one man-year.

Now, to illustrate one possible outcome of such a calculation, consider the engineering design estimates for an imaginary project. Suppose that all the individual, detailed estimates add up to 10 000 man-hours, or approximately 200 man-weeks, depending on the estimating units used. Rapid division into man-years immediately shows that five man-years must be spent in order to complete the project design.

Now assume that all the design has to be finished in the first six months of the programme and that the network shows this to be feasible. Provided that the work can be suitably scheduled, a team of ten engineers will be needed for six months, after which time they can all be switched on to other work. This is, of course, a crude exercise since there are different types of engineers with varied capabilities, and they cannot be regarded as interchangeable units.

The project manager must be relied on in this example as being a man with some experience of previous contract handling. He should at least be able to refer to records of past work, or remember previous programmes, and compare the known results with present forecasts. He could receive a rude awakening. Quite possibly, a previous contract of directly comparable size, took not ten men for six months, but ten men for one year. An apparent error of five man-years exists somewhere. This is, in any language, a king-sized problem.

Some of the reasons which cause differences of this magnitude to occur can then be analysed. But first, the initial broad check, without which the error may pass unnoticed, must be made. The project manager must always be looking for opportunities of checking and cross-checking all data presented to him. He will quickly learn by experience never to take anything entirely for granted. It is also very easy to become "lost in detail," never seeing the wood for the trees.

ESTIMATING CHARACTERISTICS OF INDIVIDUALS

As a very sound general rule, it can be taken that estimates for any work will more frequently be understated rather than overstated. Many individuals seem to be blessed with an unquenchable spirit of optimism when they are asked to predict completion times for any specific task. "I can polish off that little job in three days," is often claimed, but three weeks later only excuses have been produced. Without such optimism the world might be a much duller place in which to live and work but the project manager's lot would be much easier.

An interesting feature of optimistic estimators is the way in which they allow their cloud-cuckoo-land dreams to persist, even after completing several jobs in double the times originally forecast. They continue to churn out estimates which are every bit as hopeful as the last, and appear quite unable to learn from their previous experience. Engineers are perhaps the chief offenders in this respect, with draughtsmen running them a very close second. Fortunately the "ill wind" proverb holds good, in this situation, blowing to the good of the project manager. One source of consolation in analysing these estimates lies in the fact that they are, at least, consistent in their trend. In fact, a shrewd project manager will come to learn by experience just how pronounced the trend is in his own particular company. Better still, he will be able to apportion error factors to individuals. Typical multiplication factors usually have to be arranged to add about 50 per cent to the original estimates.

Here, then, is a project manager obtaining a set of estimates for a project, sitting down with a list of all the estimators who have been involved, and then looking up the appropriate correction factors and applying them to each figure. This may seem far-fetched but the method has been proved in practice.

Why should we not try to educate the estimators? After all, prevention is better than cure. If we did attempt such a re-education programme, the effects might vary from person to person and the known equilibrium would become upset. All of the estimators could be expected to slip back into their old ways eventually, and during the process their estimates could lie anywhere on the scale between optimism and pessimism. Arguing wastes time if nothing is achieved. Accept the situation as it exists and be grateful that it is at least predictable.

Occasionally, one may come across another kind of individual who, unlike the optimist of more customary experience, can be relied upon to give regular over-estimates of every task. This characteristic is not particularly common, and when encountered it will pay to investigate the underlying causes. Possibly the estimator lacks experience or is otherwise incompetent. These explanations are unlikely, since the typical symptom of estimating incompetence is random behaviour, and not a consistent error trend. The picture becomes clearer, if more unsavoury, when it is realised that departmental budgets are derived from estimates of project costs. Higher estimates mean (if they are accepted) bigger budgets, and expanding departments. This in turn adds to the status of the departmental heads. In these cases, therefore, E stands not only for "estimator" but also for "empire builder." Correction factors are possible but they are usually more effective when aimed not at the estimates but at their source.

Perhaps it should be granted that there is a possibility, however remote, of finding a project participant capable of providing consistent estimates for his department which are entirely accurate. The contingency is so remote that it can almost be discounted. When this rare phenomenon does occur it is apt to produce a very unsettling effect on the project manager, who has through long experience learned never to take any report at face value.

Finally there is the one remaining category of individual, that universal bane of the project manager's existence, namely the inconsistent estimator. Here we find a man who is seemingly incapable of estimating any job at all, his answers ranging from ridiculous pessimism to outrageous optimism. The only characteristic reliably displayed is in fact inconsistency. Incompetence or inexperience suggests itself as the most likely cause. Complacency could be another. Older men, looking forward to retirement rather than promotion, or staff who have been overlooked during the last handout of promotion can display these symptoms. Unfortunately, there is often a high incidence of individuals in this category at the departmental head level, just the people in fact most frequently asked to provide estimates. Only time can solve this one.

CONTINGENCIES

One common source of estimating errors can be found in the failure to appreciate that additional costs are bound to arise as a result of design errors, production mistakes, material or component failures, and the like. The degree to which these contingencies are going to add to the project costs will depend on many factors, including the type of project, the general efficiency standard of the firm, the soundness (or otherwise) of the engineering concepts, and so on. Performance on previous projects is the only reliable pointer which can be used to decide just how much to allow on each new project to cover unforseen circumstances. One could imagine that for a straightforward project, not entailing an inordinate degree of risk, the total contingency allowance might be set at 5 per cent. If the figure exceeds something like 15 per cent, perhaps the company should re-examine the desirability of tendering at a fixed price at all.

To a large extent, the additional costs which arise from contingencies are a measure of the firm's performance, and their incidence can be measured and used as a control on a long-term basis. It is probably better to set up a reserve fund from which to pay for these contingencies rather than to interfere with the original estimates. Here then is a set of standard estimates, from which tasks budgets can be derived, whilst anything extra is considered a variance.

The contingency allowance itself can be subdivided if necessary, with compartments for modifications, scrappage, rectification, and other headings, but if a sound costing system does not exist, or if the project organisation is being set up from scratch, it is wise not to attempt too much sophistication in the first place. Where an organisation does permit the separation of each type of contingency expenditure, control can be concentrated where it will do the most good. A high modification cost rate, for instance, might be shown up from cost records, and the result could be used to tighten up control on the number of modifications authorised.

ESCALATION

Every year, trade unions submit fresh wage demands, materials rise in price, transport becomes more expensive, and the staff expect their annual merit or cost-of-living awards. The whole process results in the well-known depreciation in the real value of money termed "inflation." This decay appears to be inevitable and, therefore, predictable. A project which is estimated to cost £100 000 (say) in 1970, might cost £110 000 if the start is delayed for two years.

Suppose that a project was initiated to build a new sea wall along 1000 miles of coast line at the rate of 100 miles a year. The cost of each mile of wall would gradually increase owing to the passage of time and resulting inflation. The last mile of wall completed could cost double the amount expended on the first: the costs have "escalated."

An allowance to provide for the effects of escalation must always be made for projects whose duration is expected to exceed one year. A contract tender is often prepared many months in advance of the actual starting date, and this too can lead to escalation problems. A company will safeguard itself against this possibility to some extent by placing a time limit on the validity of the price quoted in the tender, but delays in signing the contract, or in deciding the final technical details can easily add many months on to the timescale of a fairly big contract.

The actual yearly rate of any escalation allowance may have to be negotiated with the customer, especially where the contract is to be carried out for HM Government. Five per cent a year should be regarded as a minimum rate.

FIXING THE PRICE

It may be asked why it should be necessary to produce any estimates of project costs at all. Perhaps the most obvious answer, and that most frequently given, is that it is needed to fix the price. It should be realised, however, that this is by no means the whole story, and it may indeed be misleading. Timescale planning, pre-allocation of project resources, establishment of budgets and financial control, and the measurement of achievement against expected performance all demand the provision of sound estimates.

Fixing the price does, of course, depend to a very great extent on the consideration of cost predictions. It can be assumed that any company worth its salt will be equipped with a well-defined general pricing policy. Profit targets, and the relationship between costs and selling prices may be laid down very firmly. One might imagine that in these cases a fixed selling price could always be obtained by taking a set of project estimates, and adding on profit at the specified level. Life, unfortunately, is seldom quite so straightforward.

Under certain conditions a firm may be forced to accept an order, or submit a tender for a new contract at a price so low that any possibility of making a fair profit is precluded right from the start. Consider, for example, a company which is temporarily short of work, but which can predict with confidence that long-term continuity and expansion will be assured. The firm may be faced with a real dilemma: the choice lying between the dismissal of many of their staff as redundant, or keeping them on and paying their wages for no return.

Specialists and skilled men are not easy to recruit. Their training and acquired experience in a company's methods is an investment which represents a valuable part of a firm's invisible assets. Disbanding such a team can be compared to the cutting down of a mature tree. The act of chopping down and dismembering takes only a few hours, but to grow another tree of similar size must take many years. No one can tell whether the new tree will turn out to be such a fine specimen as its predecessor. In addition, of course, the survival of work groups, especially in large industries upon which local communities depend, can be seen as a moral obligation of the company concerned.

Contracts taken on to tide a firm over a lean period are termed "bridging contracts" for obvious reasons. The profit motive can, under these circumstances, be of secondary importance.

It may be expedient to submit a tender at an artificially low price in an attempt to gain entry into a market not previously exploited. There are, of course, other proven ways of achieving this end, not least of which is to take over an established firm already trading in the chosen market sector. Under-pricing, or "buying into a market," remains a common, if less drastic, alternative. One hardly needs to stress that any company which does decide to adopt a deliberate policy of price cutting will soon suffer from badly burned fingers if they have not first done their essential marketing homework.

Market conditions generally dictate the price which can be charged for any commodity, service, or project, although the exact relationship can sometimes produce surprises. In certain cases sales can actually be increased by putting prices up, contrary to all normal expectations. Usually, however, the laws of supply and demand will operate. Most project tenders must stand a better chance of acceptance if they can be kept low compared to competition. Even when a firm boasts a market monopoly and competition is entirely absent, the intensity of demand can influence the prices which can be charged. If the price tendered for a project is too high for a potential customer, he may simply decide to do without altogether. On the other side of the coin, the customary level of profit could be too low. Projects sometimes attract a high degree of risk, and it will be necessary to make sure that the price quoted allows sufficient margin to cover contingencies.

Local government authorities and other public bodies entrusted with communal funds are under strict obligations as trustees of public money. Such authorities are sometimes compelled to accept the lowest tender for any given project. If they wish to place an order at anything other than the very lowest price possible, they must have an overriding reason which they are prepared to defend.

Orders can be unwelcome because they possess nuisance value for one reason or another. Suppose for example, that a company has been asked to tender for a project at a time when the order book is already very full. This firm knows that either a very long delivery time must be quoted or, in the event of receiving an order, they will have to become involved in expensive subcontracting operations. Unless the company can foresee a rapidly expanding volume of trade, sufficient to justify raising new capital and increasing their permanent capacity, they may simply not want the order. In a case such as this the firm has a choice to make between quoting at a very high price, or not quoting at all.

Price decisions usually fall within the responsibility not of the project manager, but of the higher management of the company. The significance of cost estimates in the context of project pricing is that they provide a platform from which the profits can be gauged, relative to any specific price which may be chosen. If the estimates are shaky, there will be a tendency to increase the target profit margin in order to cover the risk. This could destroy any chance of gaining an order in a competitive market. Good sound estimates can also prove a very useful aid to the conduct of price negotiations. A contractor must know as accurately as possible just how far he can be pushed into reducing his price before his profit dwindles to useless proportions.

COST-PLUS PROJECTS

Although we have been looking exclusively at estimates with fixed price tenders as our objective, there is another type of contract which does not start off with a firm price. This is known as a "cost-plus contract," the "plus" referring to payment of an agreed fixed profit rate after measurement of the actual costs incurred each week or month.

Estimates for cost-plus projects do not require quite the same degree of accuracy as those for firm price orders. If big estimating errors are made, however, resource scheduling and timescale planning might become impossible. Large overspending of expected costs could mean death of the project if all money set aside by the customer runs out.

In cost-plus working, the customer and contractor agree the rate of profit beforehand. Thereafter the customer must be given access to the contractor's cost records, or an independent auditor be appointed to verify the contractor's claims for payment. If money is not to be regarded by the customer as flowing out of an ever-open tap, progress reporting must be carried out as accurately and faithfully as possible.

45

Cost-plus projects are becoming more rare and are, in any case, much less common than firm price work. Any project manager capable of dealing with fixed-price estimating, as outlined in this chapter, should find his task easier when the profits and not the prices are fixed.

ESTIMATING ACCURACY

Mistakes in estimating will always occur. Although they can be expected from time to time, they must never pass unnoticed, and a lesson should be learned each time. If errors consistently exceed about 10 per cent, up or down, then the project manager has a fair amount of work to do to improve matters. An achievement of plus or minus 5 per cent accuracy might be regarded as a reasonable level of estimating performance, but unfortunately some projects are too uncertain by their very nature to permit such close working.

Much has been said and written on many aspects of network analysis and other sophisticated planning aids; these will be outlined in the next chapter. Any network, however well suited to any particular application and however well drawn, will be utterly useless if it is not given the support of a good set of estimates. What is the purpose of a critical path network, for example, where the estimates are so wrong that the true critical path is shown as having two months' slack and the delivery date is even further adrift?

It has already been seen that if the degree of cost uncertainty can be reduced, the profit margin target can be cut back accordingly whenever it is necessary to compete in a vigorous market. It is not always appreciated just how much profitability can be upset by bad estimates. A simple example will show this up most clearly.

A project was sold for £10 000 against cost estimates totalling £9000. A profit margin of 10 per cent before tax was therefore budgeted. Overspending occurred, and the result was that the project finally cost £9500. This represents an estimating inaccuracy of about 5 per cent. The profit margin was slashed, however, not by 5 per cent but by 50 per cent, from £1000 to £500. This is the true magnitude of the outcome, as observed by the company's shareholders.

Profits are always vulnerable and may be subject to many variables, some of which can be predicted whilst others will come as a surprise.

The aim is to reduce the unknown variables as much as possible, and then provide a sensible allowance to cover them. Because profits are so easily destroyed, they deserve the protection of good estimates. Working on a project which has been under-estimated and where the only remaining unknown factor is the magnitude of the eventual loss can be a soul-destroying experience which not many project managers will want to suffer more than once. If such an occurrence is a direct result of their efforts, they may not be given the opportunity to try again.

4

PLANNING THE TIMESCALE

Whenever any job has to be accomplished according to a time or date deadline, then one likes to have at least some idea of the relationship between the time allowed and the time needed. This is true for any project, whether a dinner is being prepared or a motorway constructed. In the first case one would be ill-advised to tell guests that "Dinner is at seven – but the potatoes will not be cooked until seven-thirty." Similarly, there would be little point in the Minister of Transport arriving to perform the opening ceremony for Britain's newest motorway if one of the bridges still consisted of a few girders over a yawning chasm, complete with rushing torrent below.

So it is a safe assumption that a plan of some sort is always advisable, if project completion is to be assured on time. In the culinary example the planning might be very informal, consisting only of mental images in the brain of the cook. Motorways are more difficult, and have to be planned on paper.

Once a need has arisen to commit any plan to paper, a suitable notation must be adopted. Any plan, drawing, or specification which is to be read by more than one person must be regarded as a vehicle for the transmission of information. This information must be expressed in a language which is understood by all recipients if effective communications are to be established and maintained. Several notational methods and languages have been devised for timescale planning, and some of these will be examined in outline.

Time scheduling can be considered from two different viewpoints which are diametrically opposed to each other. On the one hand, a set of estimates could be obtained, and used to produce a plan from which a project completion date could be predicted. Conversely, the end-date may be predetermined, or imposed by factors outside normal control without any regard to the work content or difficulties presented. Neither situation is wholly good or bad. Schedules produced from estimates, without the application of any external pressure to compress the scale, may predict an end-date which is ludicrous from the customer's point of view, so preventing any possibility of gaining an order. If some restriction does have to be imposed on the time available, it is often possible to find a way of rescheduling the work, still keeping to the original estimates but simply changing the sequence of jobs around to shorten the overall result. Some measure of incentive to achieve a project in the shortest time reasonably possible may not be a bad thing because time really is money, and projects which are sluggish in their progress often tend to attract higher costs from fixed overheads and other causes. The situation where complete freedom is given to planners to decide their own timescale is therefore not always quite so advisable as it might at first seem.

If a plan has to be suited to some artificially determined and inflex-ible delivery requirement, all the estimates must be fitted into a fixed period of time as best as they can. A temptation is thus created for estimates to be shortened, for no better reason than that they are longer than is desirable for the purpose. If one is honest one has to admit that timescales set up by these methods will never be achieved, but they serve to pacify higher management or to gain an order from a gullible customer. Unfortunately, the truth is bound to emerge sooner or later and the consequences can only bring discredit upon the company.

Another danger which might arise from a timescale dictated by arbitrary or external factors is that the period allowed might be too long. This would be rather unusual, it is true, but by no means impossible. Extended schedules produced in this way are an ideal breeding ground for budgetary excesses according to Professor Parkinson's best-known law, where work is apt to expand to fill the time available.

Perhaps the ideal project plan is that which has been compiled by careful co-operation between all the key participants in the proposed work, with the overall agreement of the customer. To be really effective, the constituent elements must be reliably estimated and arranged in the most logical practical sequence. If pressures are exerted for the timescale to be shortened, this must be achieved

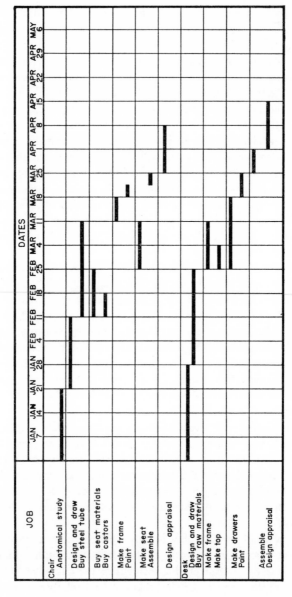

FIGURE 4.1 A SIMPLE PROJECT BAR CHART
An illustration of a type of project schedule which has
continued in widespread use for many years

50

either by a rearrangement of the work sequence, or by the deployment of additional resources. *Never* must the project manager allow himself to be persuaded or coerced into reducing an overall timescale by "marking down" estimates without any justification.

BAR CHARTS

The oldest planning technique of interest in this context involves the use of bar charts, sometimes called Gantt charts after their originator, Henry Gantt. These charts have been in widespread use as valuable planning aids for many years. Not only are bar charts easy to construct and interpret but they are readily adaptable to a great variety of planning requirements. In most factories bar charts are displayed on at least one wall, controlling functions such as development programmes, duty rotas, machine loading, training programmes, and so on.

A typical bar chart is shown in Figure 4.1. This is a very simple piece of project planning, where the timescale of a desk and chair development programme has to be controlled. Notice that the plan is drawn up on a scale which is directly proportional to calendar time. The length of each strip indicates the duration of each related task. There is, however, no direct means of indicating the dependent relationships between any one of these tasks and all the others. There is no indication, for instance, that the anatomical study must be finished before designing and drawing can begin.

For more complex charts, different coloured strips are often used to denote activities from various departments or individuals. A word of caution is necessary here, however, since there is a real danger of destroying the effectiveness of any system if it is allowed to become over-ambitious. A bar chart is above all a visual presentation of a plan, and must be capable of easy interpretation. If more than about six different colours have to be used, much of the visual impact is lost, and the method becomes difficult to administer.

Project resource scheduling is only really possible with the use of bar charts, although it is possible to construct these in an abstract form, without actually having to draw them, by using a computer. More will be said on the subject of resource scheduling later. The requirements of any particular department in terms of manpower or materials, or indeed of any other resource, can be found by

51

adding up the number of times a strip of the appropriate colour code occurs in each control period.

Several office equipment suppliers manufacture their own proprietary brands of bar charts, which can be hung on walls, and assembled from kits of parts. Some employ magnetic strips which attach themselves to a steel background, but these suffer from the serious disadvantage that a passer-by can wreck a whole schedule simply by brushing up against the board. Other schemes use plug-in plastic strips, or cardboard strips which fit into slots. A surprising number of activities can be accommodated in a small space, allowing the inclusion of a wealth of detail. One plug-in example is arranged on a 6mm ($\frac{1}{4}$ inch) grid, so that one hundred rows only occupy about 0·6m (2 feet) depth. The same scale applied laterally permits division of a sizeable timescale into periods of single weeks, or even days, without the schedule becoming too cumbersome.

With the advent of more sophisticated planning methods, notably network analysis and line of balance, Gantt charts have to some extent fallen into undeserved disrepute. Although modern techniques must usually be preferred in most situations, the older charting methods still have their uses. Planning by bar chart is infinitely better than no planning at all. The visual impact of a well-displayed schedule can be a powerful aid to controlling a simple project. There still exist many executives who demand their schedules in bar chart form because they have not learned how to interpret networks and have no intention of becoming involved in them.

NETWORK ANALYSIS

An Outline of CPA. Network analysis is the generic term for several project planning methods, of which the two most well known are PERT (programme evaluation and review technique) and CPA (critical path analysis). These systems were developed for application to large-scale "defense" projects in the USA. They were put into practical use during the late 1950s, and the striking improvements demonstrated over earlier control routines have since led to their widespread adoption in many industries far removed from either America or defence.

The heart of any network analysis technique is the arrow diagram, or "network" itself. This replaces the familiar Gantt chart, from

FIGURE 4.2 THE SIMPLEST NETWORK POSSIBLE
Two events are represented by the circles whilst the arrow
denotes the activity necessary to progress from the first
event to the second

which it differs in several important respects. Arrow diagrams are
not drawn to any linear scale. They are, however, carefully constructed to show the interdependence of each activity or task with all the
others in the project.

Figure 4.2 shows the simplest arrow diagram which it is possible
to draw. Each circle represents some programme event, such as the
start of work or completion of a task. The arrow joining the two
circles in this example indicates the activity which must take place
before the second event can be said to be achieved. Activity arrows
are always drawn from left to right, by convention, and they have no
significance in scale.

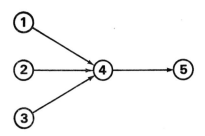

FIGURE 4.3 NETWORK RESTRICTIONS
Here, the activity leading to event 5 cannot begin until all
activities preceding event 4 have been accomplished

In Figure 4.3, another network is shown, this time containing
four activities. The numbers written within the event circles are put
there for reference purposes only, in order that we can identify any
event or activity without ambiguity. Thus the arrow from event 1 to
event 4 can be described as activity 1 to 4. In this example event 4
cannot be considered complete until all three activities leading into
it have been achieved. Only then, and not before, can activity 4 to 5

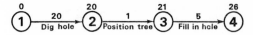

FIGURE 4.4 TREE PROJECT NETWORK
The addition of duration estimates to a network

be started. The dependence of the final activity on preceding work is therefore quite clearly highlighted.

Now, applying the method to an everyday "project," suppose that it is planned to plant a tree in the garden. If it is decided to draw a network, the result would look something like the diagram shown in Figure 4.4. The interdependence of activities is extremely important in this case and only one sequence of events is possible. The tree cannot be placed in the hole before the hole has been dug, and there would be little point in filling in the hole before positioning the tree in it.

Estimates for the duration of each activity have been made for this example, and these were –

ACTIVITY	DURATION
1–2: Dig hole	20 minutes
2–3: Position tree	1 minute
3–4: Fill in hole	5 minutes

No one needs network analysis to tell that this project is going to take twenty-six minutes to complete. Notice, however, that the estimated duration is written above each activity arrow, and the completion time for each event is arrived at by adding up these durations from left to right. The time written above the events is in each case the earliest by which each can be achieved.

Figure 4.5 reveals a slightly more complex situation where the configuration resembles a lattice or "network." Once again, estimates have been written in to indicate in weeks the duration of each activity, but this time there is more than one possible path to completion. In fact there are three routes, one of which flows through the dotted arrow, or "dummy" activity. Dummies usually have no time duration, and do not represent actual work. Rather, they denote a line of dependence between different activities, so that in this particular example the start of activity 3 to 6 could not take place before completion of both events 3 and 4.

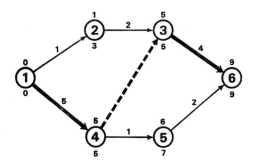

FIGURE 4.5 THE CRITICAL PATH
In this simple network, duration estimates have been
analysed to highlight the critical path, shown here by the
heavy lines

The overall project duration has once again been calculated by
addition of all activity duration estimates from left to right. Note
that in some cases there is a choice to be made, depending upon which
path is followed. The completion of event 3, for instance, could be
predicted as $1 + 2 = 3$, if the path through events 1, 2, and 3 is used,
but completion cannot really be completed until week 5 because of
the path through the dummy arrow, which is longer. Thus the
earliest possible completion time for any event is found by addition
of all preceding activities along the longest path. If this procedure
is followed right through to the end of the project, it emerges that the
duration will be nine weeks, provided, of course, that all the estimates
prove correct.

Now consider event 5. The earliest possible completion time is
week 6, leaving three weeks available before the end of the project.
It is clear that activity 5 to 6, which only needs two weeks of work,
can therefore be delayed for up to one week without upsetting the
overall timescale. This result can be indicated on the diagram by
writing the latest possible completion for event 5 underneath the
circle. The result is found this time, not by addition from left to
right, but in the exactly opposite way of subtraction from right to
left. Thus: $9 - 2 = 7$. This again can be repeated throughout the
project network until the amount of leeway or "float" on each event
can be found.

When all the time estimates and earliest and latest event times

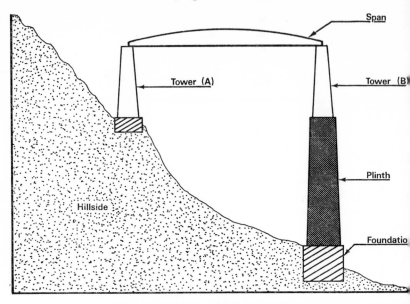

FIGURE 4.6 GANTRY PROJECT
This is a sectional view of the hillside showing the outline
requirements of the gantry project

have been added to the diagram, there will always be at least one
chain of events which have no float at all, where the earliest and
latest start times are equal. These events are critical to the successful
achievement of the project within the planned time. The route
joining these events is not surprisingly termed the "critical path."

Now to consider a slightly more substantial project, reference to
Figure 4.6 shows that a gantry has to be set up on the side of a steep
hill. This is in fact part of a much bigger project, but quite often it is
useful to draw a "sub-network" for a small section of a big project
in order to avoid the necessity for showing too much detail on the
main schedule. The requirements of this "sub-project" are quite
simple but one or two points have to be borne in mind concerning the
order in which the work is to be carried out.

The first step in erecting this gantry will be to prepare the foundations. Assume that all other preparations, including the delivery of
the materials to site, have already been carried out. Because of the
asymmetry, the two tower foundations differ in size, since one has

to bear far more weight than the other. Tower *B* has to be placed on a plinth in order to raise it to the same height as tower *A*. The final levelling adjustment is to be made after the plinth has been erected by adjusting the base height for tower *A* according to a sighting taken from the plinth top.

The special requirements are reflected in the network for this sub-project, which is shown at Figure 4.7. Dummy 8 to 4 denotes the restriction imposed on the start of the levelling at base *A*, since if the plinth were not erected, no sighting could be taken. Time estimates were made in days, and are listed below.

ACTIVITY	DURATION
1–2 : Mark out site	1 day
2–6 : Dig foundation *B*	4 days
6–7 : Concrete foundation *B*	3 days
7–8 : Erect plinth	2 days
8–9 : Erect Tower *B*	1 day
2–3 : Dig foundation *A*	2 days
3–4 : Concrete foundation *A*	1 day
8–4 : Dummy	0
4–5 : Complete base *A*	1 day
5–9 : Erect tower *A*	1 day
9–10: Erect span	1 day

When all the estimates have been written on to the network, time analysis can begin. Addition of these times from left to right allows one to determine progressively the earliest possible completion times for each event. Whenever there is a choice, with more than one activity leading into an event, the longer path must determine the earliest completion which will be possible. This is evident at events 4 and 9. By continuing the process of addition right through to the end, a total project completion of thirteen days is predicted, and this again is the earliest possible time which can be achieved.

The critical path in the gantry project is seen to run through events 1, 2, 6, 7, 8, 9, and 10. There is a float of one day on activity 8 to 9, and six days' float each on activities 2 to 3 and 3 to 4.

Now suppose that the predicted completion time of thirteen days is unacceptable to the customer, and that the shortest possible programme must be devised. It is to be assumed that additional labour can be hired, either to work in shifts or to augment the existing day teams. Crash actions to reduce activity durations usually raise project costs, and for this project cost/time forecasts have been made

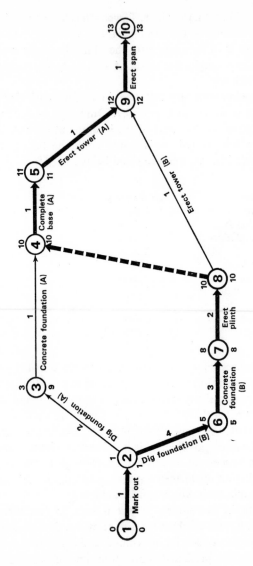

FIGURE 4.7 GANTRY PROJECT NETWORK: NORMAL DURATION
This network has been constructed using normal duration
times for all activities, with no attempt at *any* "crash"
action to shorten the timescale

58

according to the table below. Activities not included in this table are not capable of duration improvement by any means, irrespective of cost.

ACTIVITY	NORMAL DURATION	CRASH DURATION	EXTRA COST
2–6 : Dig foundation *B*	4 days	2 days	£20
6–7 : Concrete foundation *B*	3 days	2 days	£10
7–8 : Erect plinth	2 days	1 day	£5
8–9 : Erect tower *B*	1 day	½ day	£5
2–3 : Dig foundation *A*	2 days	1 day	£10
5–9 : Erect tower *A*	1 day	½ day	£5
9–10: Erect span	1 day	½ day	£5

Total cost of crashing all possible activities = £60

Figure 4.8 shows the network which results when the crash times are substituted for all activities which can be shortened by extra effort. Project duration has been reduced from thirteen days to eight days, but at the additional cost of £60. Notice, however, that activities 2–3 and 8–9 can be allowed to stay at the normal "un-crashed" durations without affecting the overall timescale improvement, since they do not lie on the critical path, and the float in each case is sufficient. The final, most economic schedule, therefore, is that shown in Figure 4.9, where the project duration is still only eight days, but the extra cost is reduced from £60 to £50.

This is a very simple example, chosen specifically to illustrate the principles of critical path analysis. In a more complex network the outcome could be far less obvious, save a great deal more unnecessary expenditure, and produce a much more effective shortening of the timescale. One often finds that during the analysis procedure crash actions along the critical path reduce the critical activity durations to such an extent that they become non-critical. Other critical paths are then thrown out, which can in turn be crashed to shorten the programme further.

Sometimes, in fact, a condition can be reached where every single path through the network becomes critical. Suppose that one path has been found which cannot be shortened beyond a certain duration, and that all the other paths through the network can be crashed to shorter times. Obviously, the first path will determine the overall project time. There will be no point at all in crashing all the other paths beyond the duration of the longest path, so it is arranged to

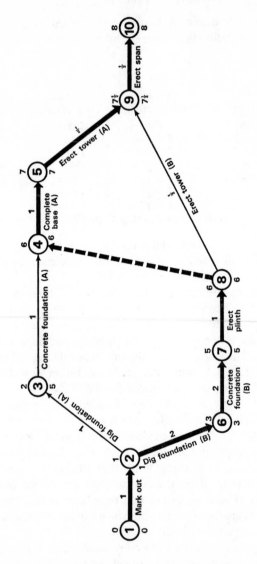

FIGURE 4.8 GANTRY PROJECT NETWORK: ALL ACTIVITIES
CRASHED TO SHORTEST TIME

All activities have been reduced to their shortest possible
durations regardless of any additional expenditure

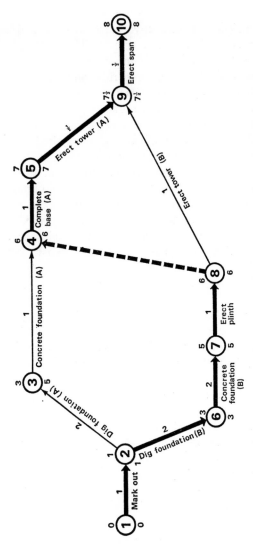

FIGURE 4.9 GANTRY PROJECT NETWORK: OPTIMISED CRASH ACTION
By careful consideration of critical activities crash action
has been limited to achieve the shortest possible duration
time without incurring the unnecessary expense of crashing
non-critical activities

61

crash them all to reach the same duration. By this means we avoid unnecessary expenditure on ineffective crash actions, and by so doing the whole network becomes critical. This represents the optimum situation from a cost-time point of view.

It is logical analysis of this type, comparing the benefits and non-benefits of spending money on crash actions, which distinguishes the critical path method from PERT. In practice, a computer can be used to carry out all the donkey-work, and the use of a computer becomes essential when rapid rescheduling is required owing to changing conditions which are beyond control.

When any network has been drawn, attention and subsequent control usually concentrates along critical activities. No time is lost in worrying about occurrences or situations which the network demonstrates to be inconsequential. Any contingency which arises can be checked against the network to establish its relevance. Only those factors which demand management action need be reported to executives in the line organisation. This is, of course, a practical demonstration of management by exception.

PERT. Programme Evaluation and Review Technique is very similar to CPA and the two methods are often confused with each other. Construction of the arrow diagrams is carried out in identical fashion for both methods, the first difference becoming apparent only when we start to estimate activity durations.

For PERT, three time estimates are required for every activity. These are –

t_o = the most *optimistic* duration

t_m = the most *likely* duration

t_p = the most *pessimistic* duration

From these three quantities, a probable time is calculated for each activity, on a statistical basis, assuming that a normal distribution curve will apply to the distribution of estimating errors.

$$t_e = \frac{t_o + 4t_m + t_p}{6} \text{ (where } t_e \text{ is the } \textit{expected} \text{ time.)}$$

This calculation is repeated on all the activities in the network, and the result used to predict the probability of completing the project within the scheduled time or not. Once more than about a hundred separate activities are included in the network, a computer becomes necessary to remove the drudgery from the calculations, and enable the results to be made available in time to allow appropriate action to be taken.

Some authorities do not accept that a normal distribution curve can be used for predicting the spread of estimating errors. It is well known that estimates are frequently too optimistic, rather than too pessimistic, and allowance can be made for this trend by skewing the curve deliberately. For this purpose, the following variation of the standard formula has been found effective –

$$t_e = \frac{t_o + 3t_m + 2t_p}{6}$$

Whichever statistical basis is chosen, the PERT network will produce a critical path in just the same way as the critical path method. The emphasis has changed, however, from cost-time analysis to a statistical prediction of completion probability against time. Although many users of network techniques refer to their networks as PERT, it is the CPA method which is now in widest use, and the term PERT is often misapplied. Possibly, with estimating accuracies leaving much to be desired, and with contingencies popping up all over the place, the PERT system is just a shade too academic, and removed from practicability when compared to CPA.

SHORTENING THE TIMESCALE BY REARRANGING THE NETWORK

If a timescale does emerge which exceeds the time available, there are several ways in which rescheduling can help, often without recourse to expensive crash action. One example is illustrated in Figure 4.10, where a small part of a large network has been considered. Three activities are involved: design engineering, drawing, and the procurement of materials. When time estimates were apportioned it was found that the overall project time was unacceptably long. These three activities were included among those which lay along the critical path. Their contribution to the project duration appeared to be twenty-eight weeks as indicated in Figure 4.10a.

By employing more engineers and draughtsmen, and by taking special procurement steps, it would be possible to shorten these activities, but only at some additional expense. But is such expenditure necessary? Re-examination of the logic uncovers a fundamental

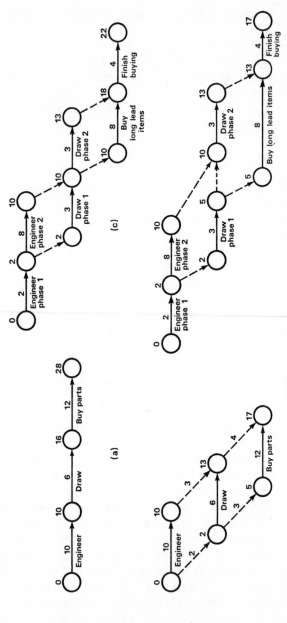

FIGURE 4.10 LADDER NETWORKS
Different logical interpretations of activities which can be allowed to overlap

misconception. It may be asked if all engineering must be completed before drawing can even start. Of course this is not so. The activities can be allowed to overlap to some extent. Similarly, some of the long-lead purchased items can be ordered in advance, as soon as the engineers have specified them. It is not necessary to wait until the final parts lists have been drawn and issued.

In Figure 4.10*b* an attempt has been made to indicate the overlap of activities by the use of dummies, each of which has been given a duration value. Drawing can start two weeks after the start of engineering, but cannot be completed until three weeks after the completion of engineering. Purchasing, in this example, can begin as soon as the long-lead items are specified, three weeks after the start of drawing. Some purchased items cannot be ordered, however, until the final general assembly drawing has been completed, with the complete parts list. These late items are expected to arrive four weeks after the completion of drawing. Although no crash action has been planned, the timescale is reduced by almost half, to seventeen weeks.

Overlapping activities, where one is dependent upon a continual flow of work or information from the other, are called "ladder activities." Strictly speaking, the logic of this network, as shown in Figure 4.10*b*, would not stand up to close scrutiny. One might assume that drawing could start two weeks after week 0, even if no engineering had been carried out, and that procurement could be started at week 5, whatever the state of engineering or drawing. Clearly, this was not the intention of the planners when the network was drawn, and alternative networks might be suggested.

In Figure 4.10*c*, the same sequence of activities has been depicted, but by splitting engineering up into two phases, and doing the same with drawing, the true relationships and restrictions are more clearly demonstrated. But a different, and wrong, answer has been obtained this time. The error lies in the start restriction imposed upon procurement, which is in fact not dependent upon the completion of engineering, but only upon phase 1 of the drawing activity. The true picture is obtained by drawing the network of Figure 4.10*d*, where the dummies have been correctly placed.

By rearranging the logic, therefore, it is possible to achieve realistic improvements in timescale at no additional cost. As illustrated in Figure 4.10, however, care must be taken to write down the correct logic, otherwise wrong answers will result. In practice, the simpler

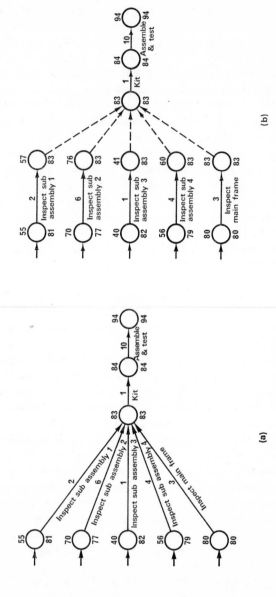

FIGURE 4.11 USING DUMMIES TO EXTEND DISPLAYED INFORMATION
In diagram (b) the activities preceding the kitting activity
can be analysed individually because their end events
have been separated by the addition of dummies

66

ladder network of Figure 4.10*b* is taken to mean what was intended, by convention. This is sometimes denoted by marking the end events with squares instead of circles.

USE OF DUMMIES TO IMPROVE NETWORK CLARITY

Dummies can often be added to a network in order to clarify or extend the information displayed. One example is shown in Figure 4.11, where the final stages of a project network are illustrated. In Figure 4.11*a* the earliest possible finish for each sub-stage inspection activity cannot be shown. By inserting dummies, as shown in Figure 4.11*b*, the end events can be drawn in. Now suppose that this project has reached the final kitting stage, and that the network is being used by production control as a direct aid to progressing the work. In the Figure 4.11*a*, any one of the sub-stage activities might be holding up the kitting stage, but it is not easy to indicate which. If dummies have been added, end events can be coloured in or crossed off as they are achieved. Outstanding activities can therefore be highlighted on the visual display. These comments do not apply to networks which will be processed by computer, as dummies add to processing time and cost.

STANDARD NETWORKS

It is possible that several projects will be handled by a company which, although different in size, follow the same general pattern. In such circumstances, the use of "standard" networks can sometimes be adopted. An example of work which might qualify for "standard" networks would be the construction of identical detached houses, on different sites. Whilst the same network configuration could be applied to every house, the duration of certain activities would vary according to site conditions. Another example is provided by the network describing laboratory development of almost identical products, where company policy and practice defines all the activities which must take place.

The "standard" network technique is carried out by first drawing up a master "skeleton" network covering all activities required for the typical project. Duration estimates are not added to the master. When each project materialises, a sub-master is printed from the original master, and edited or augmented as necessary. Durations and time data are then assessed and entered on the specific network.

It can be argued, with much justification, that any concept of "standard" networks is a contradiction in terms. Networking is, after all, supposed to inspire logical thought, and was never intended to regiment planning into a stereotyped routine where constructive imagination is thwarted. Nevertheless, when time is short, standard networks can sometimes prove such time-savers that they will be used where the networking process might otherwise have been circumvented altogether.

Figure 4.12 illustrates a "standard" network skeleton which was developed for the control of fairly complex projects varying in size, cost, and duration. The work involves the planning, supply, and installation of factory produced hospital operating theatres. The theatres vary in size, and the number to be supplied for any contract might range from single theatres to multi-theatre suites.

The operating theatre network covers many types of activity, including contract engineering, factory production, subcontract work, purchasing, and installation. When more detail is required, as in the case of building activities, for instance, other contractors will be expected to produce their own sub-networks. The main theatres are erected within the outside building shell, and the use of standard production components, assembled on a modular principle, reduces the areas of uncertainty in factory activities.

This particular network was drawn during a whole-day network training session which all key departmental heads, drawn from several company locations, attended. The initial meeting was difficult to organise, owing to the usual limitations experienced when trying to assemble several people at one time and place when all the individuals lead a busy commercial existence. However, the investment was indeed a sound one, resulting in the subsequent saving of many planning hours.

THE NETWORKING SESSION

When a network is drawn, it is customary and desirable to have at least one expert on hand from each department likely to be involved in the project being planned. The individuals chosen should be of sufficient seniority to enable them to commit their departments to any methods of working or estimates which might be agreed during the networking session. The network itself can be drawn on a blackboard, but usually a roll of paper fixed to a wall will be found more useful. Networks have a habit of overflowing beyond the edges of blackboards, but it is a relatively simple matter to extend a paper diagram. Charcoal or a broad felt-tipped pen should be used to draw the lines, so that everyone can see exactly what is going on. When the session has been completed, and the network is finished, the paper can be taken away to a drawing office and copied or traced so that it can then be printed and distributed.

Every well-run meeting should have a chairman and a networking session is no exception. Usually, the project manager will adopt this role and he will also draw the network, acting on the advice and instructions of all members of the team. He can use his own experience to steer the preparation of the diagram along the right lines, asking check questions from time to time in order to prove the network logic.

Sometimes the proceedings can be started by drawing the "project completed" event at the right edge of the paper and then proceeding backwards towards the start. The questions are then asked in the form: "what must have been done immediately before this stage is reached?" The answer to the first question of any series would probably be either "customer handover" or "final inspection" – activities often overlooked during the planning stage. In some cases starting from the end event provides a better basis for the imagination to work on. This is not true of all projects, and the method adopted must depend upon the nature of the work, and also upon the personal preference of the planner. Some experimentation in this direction may prove worth while.

When duration estimates are added to the network, some authorities suggest that activities should be estimated at random. Sequential working, from left to right along paths, could lead to an early awareness of possible critical events or programme overruns. In other words, the impartiality of the estimators could become impaired, the estimates being influenced by project demands rather than by the true work content of each job. Any temptation to assume that scheduled activity durations can be shortened by the inclusion of overtime working should be avoided wherever possible. Whilst overtime certainly can be used in this way, it must always be regarded as a reserve resource, to be held back against unforeseen contingencies.

NETWORK ANALYSIS AS A BASIC TOOL

Networking demands the application of sound common sense and very little else. The mystique which has been allowed to grow up around the method may have its origin in the specialised jargon and terminology which was developed along with PERT and CPM. In fact, there is no mystery, and no special degree of intelligence is required. Any individual endowed with his fair share of mental aptitude could be expected to become acquainted with at least a working knowledge of arrow diagram preparation in just one day. The method of teaching is, however, all important; the premature introduction of all but the basic bones of the systems must be avoided.

Those who choose to go through project life in ignorance of the finer points of networking language may find themselves at some disadvantage if called upon to discuss problems or networking generally with their more erudite colleagues. Every profession has its own language, and without it communication must suffer. Nevertheless, the actual application of critical path techniques can be conducted very effectively, provided that the logical concepts are properly appreciated. Network analysis is a simple but valuable management tool which should never be regarded as a complicated and advanced technique reserved for the specialist.

The benefits to be derived from the construction of a network are in themselves often worth while, even if no duration estimates are made, and the network is not followed up for controlling subsequent progress. Networking encourages a logical progression of thinking and planning. Not only is a notational method provided, which allows expression of all inter-activity dependencies and relationships, but there is a distinct possibility that some activities may be brought to light which might otherwise have been excluded from schedules, estimates, and, most important, price build-up.

It would be unreasonable and unrealistic to expect the project manager to carry out network planning in isolation. He must be able to count upon the co-operation and support of members from every department in the company. This applies not only to the planning sessions, but also to subsequent discussions and progress monitoring. This support will only be possible if suitable training has been provided. Once the idea of network analysis has been accepted throughout a company, most of the battle will have been won.

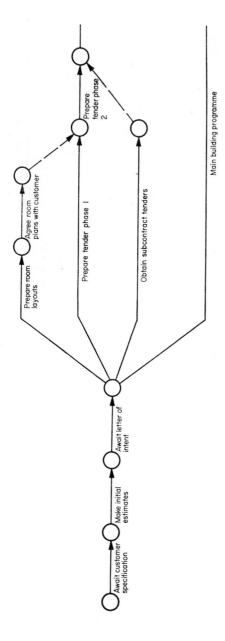

FIGURE 4.12 STANDARD NETWORK (*continued on pages 72–5*)
A network produced for repetitive use on consecutive
operating theatre projects. The basic network is augmented
or edited as necessary for each new project before the
addition of estimates

(*By courtesy of Honeywell Controls Limited*)

71

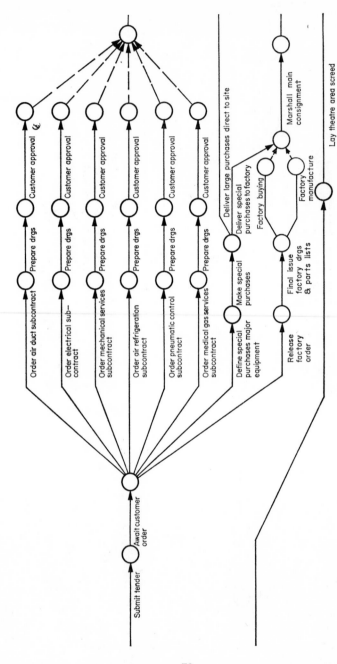

FIGURE 4.12 *continued*

72

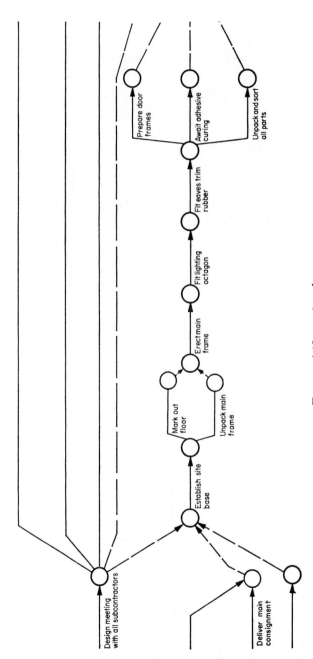

FIGURE 4.12 continued

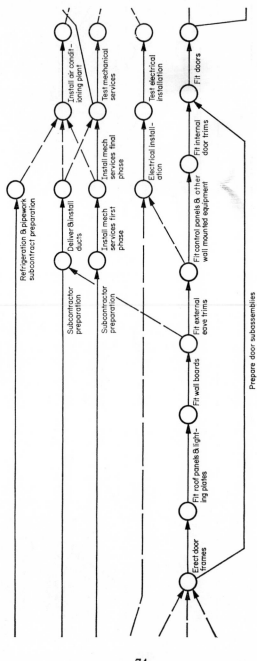

FIGURE 4.12 *continued*

74

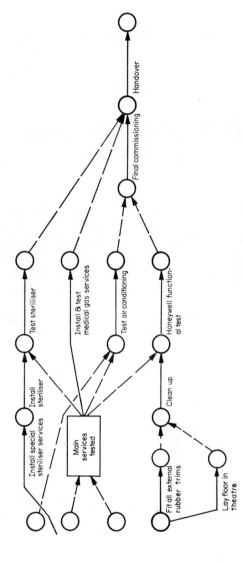

FIGURE 4.12 *concluded*

75

5

SCHEDULING RESOURCES
AND PARTS

A network cannot normally be used by itself to demonstrate the volume of resources needed at any given point in project time. In fact, when the network is drawn up, no account is ever taken of the resources which will be available. Any restriction on the start of an activity is usually assumed to be dependent only upon the completion of previous related events, and not on the existence of suitable men at the right time.

Naturally, if a planning team is aware that, for the sake of argument, four fitters are employed in one particular department, they would be unlikely to estimate a non-critical activity duration at a level which presumed the employment of more than four men from that department. However, the existence of other activities, possibly occurring simultaneously, and also requiring the use of fitters from the same department, would not be considered. Although the network drawn up might be fine in logical theory, it could prove to be completely impossible to carry out in practice.

Resource considerations can, for the purposes of scheduling, be extended to include not only labour, but also all other resources. Space, money, and the supply of bulk materials could all be dealt with alongside the manpower schedules but for reasons of clarity the following discussions will be concentrated on labour scheduling. Treatment of other resources would be similar except, of course, that the units of quantity will change.

CASE STUDY: GARAGE PROJECT

The problems and principles of resource scheduling can be

76

introduced and explained by considering a simple construction project. A small firm of builders has been commissioned to erect a detached garage. The building is to be constructed of brick, with a corrugated asbestos roof. This roof, of lean-to design, will incorporate some transparent sheets instead of windows. The doors are to be timber framed, and hung on strap hinges. The overall size of the completed garage will be approximately 6 metres (or yards) long by 3m wide by 2·5m high, so that any man-handling of materials will never demand the use of more than two men, since no long spans or other heavy components are involved.

Figure 5.1 shows the network diagram which was evolved for the project. The duration of all the activities has been estimated with a small labour force in mind, typically consisting of one skilled craftsman, aided wherever necessary by a labourer. No consideration has been given to the simultaneous occurrence of activities, and the corresponding resources implied. Under these conditions, assuming that all the earliest start dates can be achieved and that no limitation or resources exists, the project should take twenty-four working days. This timescale also assumes that all materials had previously been delivered to the site. The network does not indicate how many men must be employed to achieve this result.

When an attempt is made to determine the labour requirements, the first step is to convert the network diagram into a bar chart. This result, for the garage project, is shown in Figure 5.2. In this bar chart two different grades of labour have been scheduled: skilled and unskilled. Such diagrams can be drawn to a scale of 5 or 10mm (or ¼ inch) to each working day. Horizontal strips have been used to denote project activities, and each represents the employment of one man. The colour of the strips indicates the grade of labour to be used on any particular activity. If more than one man is to be allocated to any task, the appropriate number of strips have been positioned side by side.

The timescale has been arranged to take weekend rests into account. If necessary, Saturday mornings, not shown on the chart, could be considered as an extra amount of available time to be held in reserve against unforeseen contingencies. Similarly, each day is taken to account for only eight working hours, so that any evening overtime can also be held as a reserve resource. Naturally, when reserves are held back in this way, the budget must contain corresponding allowances. Notice that the inclusion of weekends has

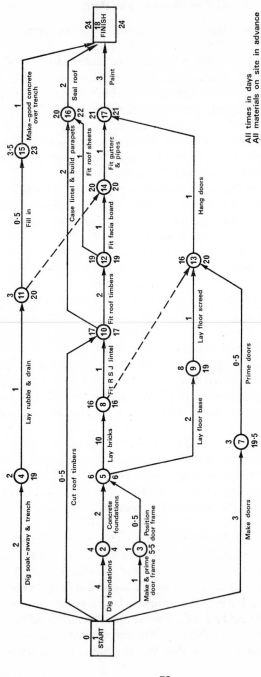

FIGURE 5.1 GARAGE CONSTRUCTION NETWORK
Although this network indicates a project duration of
twenty-four days, resource limitations could delay some
activities and prolong the project

78

extended the total timescale, so that the network time of twenty-four working days has become thirty-two calendar days.

The bar chart of Figure 5.2 was drawn not so much with regard to the resources which were available at the time as to indicate what resources would be required in order to fulfil the programme indicated by the network. Each activity has been shown starting at the earliest possible time, without any regard to the possibility of slipping non-critical activities in order to reduce resource requirements. The resources which would be needed to carry out this plan are shown at the foot of each column. These figures were calculated by adding up the number of times by which strips of each colour occurred in the period columns. When half-strips were encountered, indicating the use of a man for only half a day, they were counted as whole man-days unless it was found possible to pair them with complementary half-days occurring in the same period.

The pattern of resources required to execute the programme according to the bar chart is shown by the figures at the bottom of all the columns, but demonstrated much more clearly by the histogram of Figure 5.3. The result is shown to be, to say the least, unsatisfactory. On some days men are expected to be idle. On others, three men will be required, but only for a short time. The work load is too uneven for profitable comfort. Either the firm has to be able and willing to switch men around at short notice, between different contracts, or the unprofitable alternative of paying men for idle time must be tolerated.

It is possible, and desirable, to make some attempt at improving the practicability of a resource schedule by rearranging the activities. The approach to this operation must be governed by the most significant planning objectives. These can be summarised as follows –

1   To plan for fixed, but limited resources, accepting that this might inevitably extend the timescale

2   To assume that unlimited resources could be brought in, using subcontract labour where necessary, so that no slip in the overall programme need occur. The scheduling, however, must be carried out sensibly, to remove all peaks and troughs in scheduled requirements which are not essential to completing the project on time

3   To adopt a compromise solution, allowing a limited

79

FIFURE 5.2 GARAGE PROJECT RESOURCE SCHEDULE BEFORE LEVELLING
This schedule corresponds exactly to the network of Figure 5.1 and allows all activities to start at the earliest possible times. The figures at the foot of each column show the uneven nature of the resource requirements

80

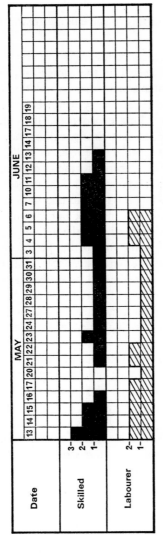

FIGURE 5.3 GARAGE PROJECT RESOURCE HISTOGRAM BEFORE LEVELLING
The histogram emphasises the uneven resources which
would be needed to achieve the schedule shown in Figure 5.2

81

programme extension if absolutely necessary, whilst
agreeing to the drafting of some limited extra resources

To take first the situation where resources are very limited, suppose
that the building firm engaged on the garage project is a very tiny
outfit, comprising the not unusual father-son relationship. The father,
no longer capable of sustained heavy work, is nevertheless a good
all-round craftsman with long experience. The son, on the other
hand, can best be described as a strong, willing lad, sound in wind
and limb, but lacking any special experience or skill.

Taking this particular case, therefore, the firm's total resources can
be listed as: skilled men: 1; labourers: 1. If the project is to be carried
out solely by this small team, it is obvious that the schedule displayed
in the bar-chart of Figure 5.2 cannot be implemented. Accordingly,
the schedule must be rearranged. All the activities can be shuffled
around until the figures at the foot of the period columns add up
to no more than the limited resources available. Notice that when the
bar chart is constructed or reshuffled, the original restraints of the
network must still be observed. Figure 5.4 shows the revised chart,
and it is easily seen that the timescale has had to be extended by
eight working days. Thus the total calendar time has been increased
to forty-four days.

The histogram of resources which corresponds to the revised bar
chart is shown at Figure 5.5. This indicates a perfect schedule for the
firm, since there are no idle days shown and no unwelcome peaks.
The new schedule may not, however, be so acceptable to a potential
customer, who is awaiting delivery of his new car and wants to ensure
that it will be safely garaged at night. Not unreasonably, if he cannot
have his garage erected within a short space of time he may decide
to place his order with a larger firm.

Several courses of action are open to the small builder. Among
these are the following –

1   Work to the longer timescale, using only the available
resources, but make a false promise to the customer
that the job will be finished in thirty-two calendar days

2   Tell the customer the unvarnished truth – and lose the
order

3   Revert to the resource schedule first devised, as shown

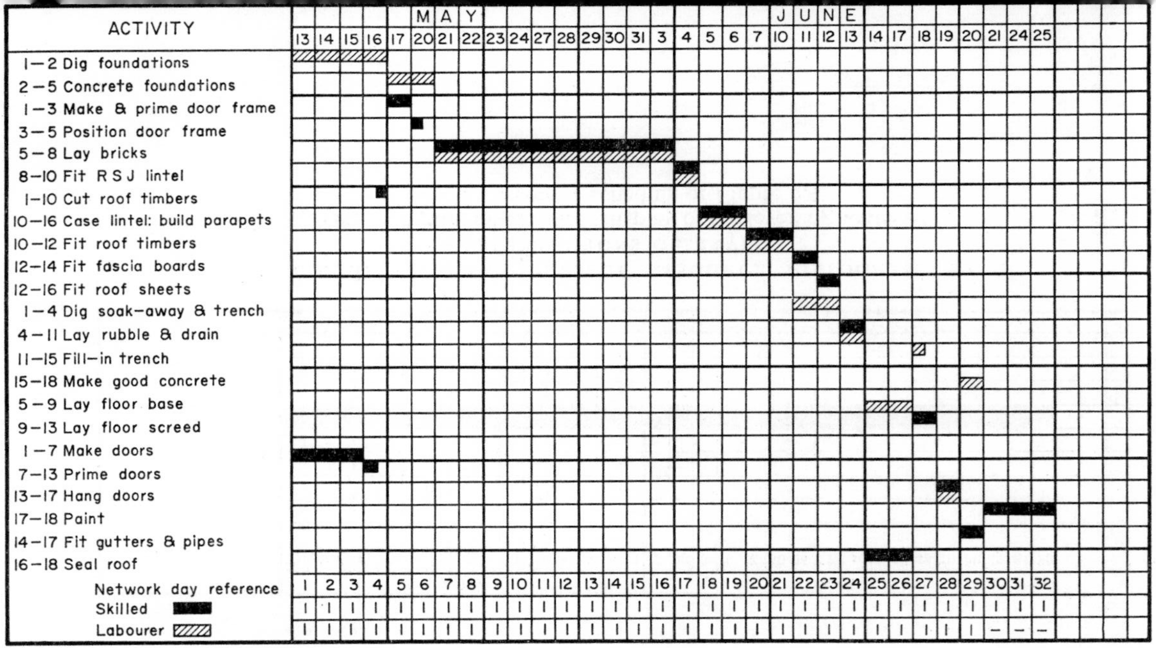

FIGURE 5.4 GARAGE PROJECT RESOURCE SCHEDULE LEVELLED TO
USE AVAILABLE RESOURCES

The garage can now be built with the limited resources
available but the project duration has been extended.
Network restrictions have still been observed

83

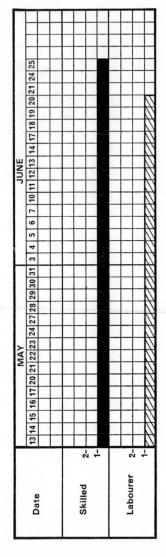

FIGURE 5.5 GARAGE PROJECT RESOURCE HISTOGRAM WITH
RESTRICTIONS OBSERVED

The histogram gives a clear display of the levelling achieved
by the resource schedule of Figure 5.4

84

in Figures 5.2 and 5.3, taking on additional men for the
period regardless of cost

4   Take on additional men, but first level out the resource
schedule to remove most of the peaks and troughs

A study of the bar chart shown in Figure 5.6, together with the resulting histogram of Figure 5.7, shows that it is, in fact, possible to
reschedule the activities to obtain a resource usage pattern which is
more acceptable. The bar chart is still governed by the original
network. This means that no shuffling of critical activities can be
tolerated if the timescale is to remain unaltered. The only adjustment
possible is of non-critical activities, and these can only be moved
backwards or forwards according to the restraints imposed upon
them by the network.

Notice that these restraints are not only composed of the logical
rules, as shown by the relative positioning of arrows and events.
Each activity is only free to move in time between the earliest and
latest possible times shown at the start and end events. The amount
by which each activity can be moved without affecting the completion time is called the "float." It is this float which really determines
the degree of flexibility open to the planners during resource levelling
operations.

ACTIVITY FLOAT AND RESOURCE SCHEDULING

The concept of float, and the specific definitions for the three
possible variations, is sometimes difficult to comprehend. Since
one of the more practical applications of float is found during the
resource scheduling process, it is convenient to illustrate and define
float in some detail at this point. The network for the garage project,
as shown in Figure 5.1, will provide a suitable example.

First, consider activity 9 to 13 "lay floor screed." For convenience,
this activity has been extracted from the network and shown
separately in Figure 5.8. Although the activity is isolated from the
remainder of the network in this diagram, all the data relevant to
float is included. A glance at event 9 shows that the earliest possible
start is at day 8, whilst the latest possible start is on day 19. The
activity therefore has a total possible leeway, or float of eleven days.
This is called the "total float."

85

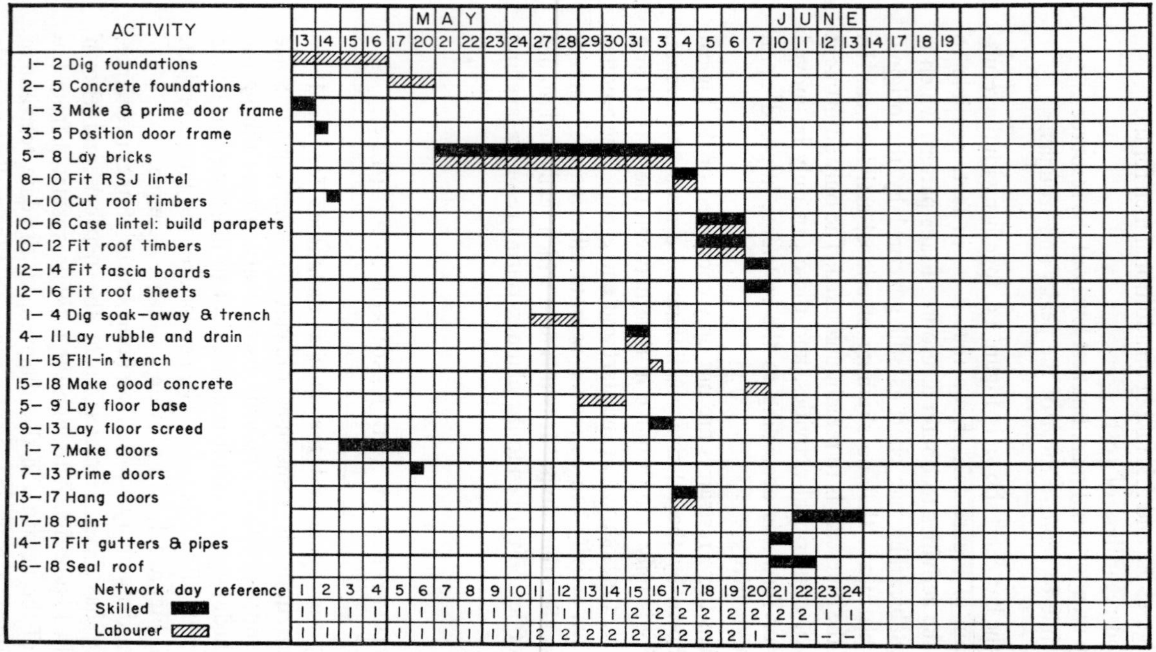

FIGURE 5.6 GARAGE PROJECT RESOURCE SCHEDULE LEVELLED TO ACHIEVE EARLIEST FINISH

Here the project can be completed within the network's timescale. By shuffling activities around within their network limitations the undue peaks shown in Figures 5.2 and 5.3 have been removed

86

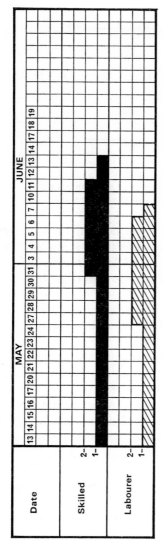

FIGURE 5.7 GARAGE PROJECT RESOURCE HISTOGRAM LEVELLED
FOR EARLIEST FINISH

Compare this histogram with that shown in Figure 5.3. The
same project duration can be achieved but the benefits
derived from resource levelling show up dramatically in
the smoother requirement pattern

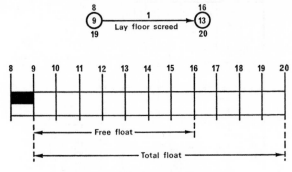

FIGURE 5.8 GARAGE PROJECT
Float analysis of activity 9–13

If the floor screed operation is delayed up to the amount allowed by the total float, some, if not all, of the float available for following activities will be used up. The total float for any activity is therefore dependent upon, and also affects, the float of other linked activities.

Total Float. This is formally defined as the amount of float available when all preceding activities take place at the earliest possible times and all following activities are allowed to occur at the latest indicated times.

Although the total float for activity 9 to 13 happened to be equal to the difference between the earliest and latest start times for event 9, this cannot always be taken as a reliable guide to the amount of total float available for any activity. A study of the formal definition just given, with an examination of another activity taken from the garage network will show that the influence of other network restrictions can easily upset this simple situation.

In Figure 5.9, activity 10 to 16, "case lintel and build parapets," has been isolated and analysed. It is seen that although event 10 is critical, and cannot itself float, the whole activity does possess a degree of float. The end and start events for this activity have been separately influenced by other network factors.

The actual float conditions are illustrated best in the small segment of bar chart which is included in Figure 5.9. It is apparent from this diagram that when the formal definition is literally applied, the total available float for activity 10 to 16 is three days. It is not difficult to derive the simple expression necessary to calculate this float when the bar chart segment and activity arrow in Figure 5.9 are compared.

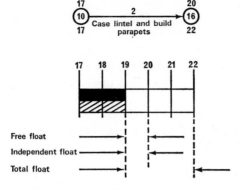

FIGURE 5.9 GARAGE PROJECT
Float analysis of activity 10–16

Total float = latest possible end-event time – earliest
possible start-event time – the activity
duration

Applying the data from Figure 5.9 to this formula –
Total float (activity 10 to 16) = (22 – 17 – 2) = 3 days

Returning to the network diagram, suppose that the floor screed activity (9 to 13) must be delayed owing to the absence of available workmen at the right time. The network shows that the activity "hang doors" cannot in any case start before day 16 because of the restriction imposed by event 8, via the dummy arrow. This means that the floor screed activity could be started as late as day 15 before any ill effects were caused to following activities. There is a leeway of seven days over which the activity is free to move, provided of course that all preceding events are achieved at the earliest possible times. This period of seven days is termed the "free float" for activity 9 to 13.

Free Float. This is formally defined as the amount of float available when all preceding activities take place at the earliest possible times and all following activities can also take place at the earliest possible times.

Free float = earliest possible end-event time – earliest
possible start-event time – the activity
duration

89

Now consider activity 10 to 16 once again, as shown in Figure 5.9. Notice that there exists a possibility of shuffling this activity around over a one day period whatever happens to the schedule for all other network activities. It matters not whether the preceding events are all allowed to run up to their latest possible times or the following events are to start at their earliest times. This activity can still be moved backwards and forwards by a total amount of one day before any other network activity is affected. This small amount of float, because it is independent of all surrounding activities, is called "independent float."

Independent Float. This is formally defined as the amount of float available when all preceding activities take place at the latest possible times and all following activities take place at their earliest possible times.

$$\text{Independent float} = \text{earliest possible end-event time} - \\ \text{latest possible start-event time} - \\ \text{the activity duration}$$

The incidence of independent float is rare. Usually, when the above formula is applied to any activity in a network the result is either negative or zero.

RESOURCE SCHEDULING BY COMPUTER

The case study just described would present no great difficulty to a scheduler armed with an adjustable bar chart and all the relevant project facts. Proprietary kits are indeed available for this purpose. One example makes use of plastic strips which can be obtained in a range of colours, and cut to any desired length. A baseboard is provided, enabling the strips to be plugged into holes which are arranged on a grid pattern.

Projects up to about 100 activities in complexity can be scheduled manually, using an adjustable board. The job might occupy a couple of days and inflict a peculiar type of eye-strain on the scheduler, but nevertheless could be used. The method would, however, be inflexible, since any change of plans must involve tedious manipulation of all the coloured strips every time. For really large projects, manual resource scheduling is impracticable, and the work must be entrusted to a modern business computer.

Before any project can be scheduled by computer, the project manager has to ensure that certain basic facilities are available to him. These include a suitable computer installation, a practical program or "software" package, operating staff at the computer who are skilled in data processing networks, and good communications between the computer and the user. Owing to the efforts of several computer manufacturers and software consultants these facilities are within the reach of even the smallest companies, without any need for capital investment. International Computing Services Limited, for example, have set up several highly effective bureaux within the UK. The Civil Engineering Department of the Loughborough University of Technology has carried out a useful survey of available services, and the results are published in their User's Report number 5.

The user will often be able to agree a design of output report page with the computer team which suits his needs best. The ability of the computer to sort and collate data into any desired sequence will be found invaluable. It will be possible, for instance, to ask for a report which lists all activities, with dummies excluded, in order of their scheduled start dates. Resource requirements can be printed out on a day-by-day basis. Cost control data can be linked to the schedule, and it will also be possible to schedule several projects simultaneously, within the common pool of resources available.

The data processing experts will be able to provide the necessary instruction in the preparation of input data. They will also advise the user on the range of facilities and reports which can be prepared.

The cost of computing services will depend on many factors, but it is possible to produce a comprehensive schedule for projects totalling over 2000 activities for less than £200. Costs will be minimised if the input data is free of errors, so that expensive error runs are avoided. The need for up-dating reports should not be assumed essential on a periodic basis. If a good schedule exists and is adhered to, it will only have to be up-dated when a new project is added. Contrary to the advice given on page 67, the use of too many dummies can inflate the cost of each run, so that the networks drawn specifically for computer operation will have as few dummies as possible. If reasonable precautions are taken along these lines, the cost of computer scheduling should be held between $\frac{1}{2}$ and 1 per cent of project costs. This is a small price to pay for the very effective schedules which result.

SCHEDULES GOOD AND BAD

Whether resources are to be planned by computer or manually, each schedule must always be based upon a logical and feasible timescale, preferably derived from a network. Unfortunately, this principle is not always fully appreciated. In many companies, project managers, engineers, and other planners will be found drawing up impressive-looking histograms, covering forecasts for many weeks or months ahead, without the slightest logical justification for what they are writing down. It is no use trying to predict resource schedules down to the last man, when the basic estimates or planning concepts are themselves unsound. Long-term plans produced by these methods run the risk of being out-dated within days of their inception.

If any firm did ever attempt to introduce and implement a resource schedule which was either uneven or impracticable, one can assume that common sense would prevail – at least to some extent. When men were shown to be idle on the chart, in practice they would not really stand around with hands pocketed. Rather, if for no reason other than boredom, they would attempt to make themselves useful somehow. The end-result could, in effect, lead to trial and error. A significant measure of success could be expected from these amateur attempts, especially in a small contract.

In a very small project therefore, such as the garage project, the work team can sort themselves out very effectively. The whole extent of the work is sufficiently compact to enable each man to visualise the complete operation. It is true that instances will arise when men will fall over each other and find wet paint or unset concrete to hinder their efforts. Nevertheless, provided the work is not extensive and the work team is small, there is really no need at all to produce a resource schedule.

Now suppose that instead of the small construction project, aimed at the completion of one private-car garage, the building contractor was asked to construct a factory building, 10 000m² (about 108 000 square feet) in extent, and to a short timescale. Scheduling might have to take into account the bulk deliveries of materials to site, the hiring of plant and other equipment, and the assembly of a sizeable work force. No one man in this team could be expected to visualise the whole project mentally. A logical preplanned work schedule becomes essential.

When the unworkable schedule was introduced into the small project, the men sorted themselves out successfully. They did, however, ignore the schedule, and consequently disobeyed their instructions. If a bad work schedule were to be imposed upon a large work force, demanding peak loads which were impossible to meet, or making groups of men idle for long periods, then the same process might take place. The schedule might well be discarded as the men attempted to sort themselves out. This time the results, although possibly a good basis for a comedy sketch, might not be so amusing to watch. The genuine, but amateur, attempt at rescheduling could cause a deterioration of the whole situation, leading to a final usage of resources more wasteful and unproductive than that indicated even by the bad schedule.

Whenever a resource schedule is planned, therefore, it must be examined critically in the light of all known project restrictions and conditions to ensure that it is feasible. If, in spite of these precautions, the plan does prove to be less than perfect, rapid rescheduling must be carried out to remove any anomalies as soon as they are discovered. At all costs, the situation where continuous attempts are being made to operate according to an unworkable schedule must be avoided. Otherwise control will be lost. When control is lost in this way, it may not be possible to retrieve the situation, since the project conditions will have become random and unknown. There will be no basis on which to rebuild.

SCHEDULING PARTS

The parts and materials needed for any project can, of course, be considered as much a part of the resources necessary to complete that project as the labour content. As such, the materials must be included within any overall scheduling arrangements. Whilst Chapter 6 is devoted exclusively to problems of materials control, there is another aspect of parts scheduling which falls more logically into the realm of resource allocation.

This becomes apparent if all parts and materials are taken into account, including not only those which are to be purchased from outside sources, but also those piece parts, assemblies and sub-assemblies which must be manufactured within the contractor's own organisation. In other words, materials control is a technique which

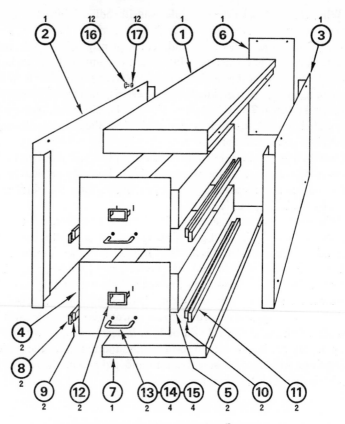

FIGURE 5.10 FILING CABINET PROJECT
An exploded view to show the constituent parts needed
for a two drawer filing cabinet

is more usually associated with bought-out materials and components, but one also has to consider the wider overall aspect for ensuring that every single item of hardware is available as and when required, whatever its source.

To a large extent, if all the labour forces are scheduled sensibly, and the supporting raw materials are made available in accordance with immediate production demands, the production of piece parts and assemblies should fall into line automatically with project needs. There are, however, one or two exceptions to this rule. Difficulties are created, for instance, when a project is aimed not at the com-

ITEM NO	PART NUMBER	DESCRIPTION	QTY	REMARKS		
1	FC/1001	Top plate	1			
2	FC/1002/L	Side plate, L/H	1			
3	FC/1002/R	Side plate, R/H	1			
4	FC/1003	Drawer front	2			
5	FC/1004	Drawer chassis	2			
6	FC/1005	Rear plate	1			
7	FC/1006	Plinth	1			
8	A 502−A	Runner, outer, L/H	2	Bought−out. Smiths Ltd		
9	A 502−B	Runner, inner, L/H	2	"	"	
10	A 503−B	Runner, inner, R/H	2	"	"	
11	A 503−A	Runner, outer, R/H	2	"	"	
12	A 209	Title card holder	2	"	Carter & Coy	
13	A 350	Handle	2	"	Epsom & Salt Ltd	
14	S 217	Screw	4	"	Acme Screw Co Type 347M−F	
15	W 180	Washer, shakeproof	4	"	Acme Screw Co Type 459SP	
16	S 527	Screw, self tapping	12	"	Acme Screw Co Type 1003ST−X	
17	W 180	Washer, shakeproof	12	"	Acme Screw Co Type 459SP	

Iss	Mod No	Date	Sig	Iss	Mod No	Date	Sig	Iss	Mod No	Date	Sig
1	First	6−5−68									

Drawn by EFP	Checked AJP	Approved *OL Lock*	Date 1−5−68	

ROBINSON'S OFFICE FURNITURE COMPANY LIMITED, BIRMINGHAM

Title Filing cabinet−Elite series−2 drawer without lock	Sheet 1 of 1 sheets	Assembly number FC/1000

FIGURE 5.11 SIMPLE PARTS LIST FOR FILING CABINET
This list was produced by counting up the parts shown in
the exploded view with no regard to production subassembly requirements

95

pletion of only one unit, but requires a series of identical or similar assemblies to be made over a period of time, according to some complex delivery schedule. Here, the project is transformed into something which lies between the one-off type of manufacture, and repetitive batch production.

Other problems can be generated when a single complex project contains parts which are common to many of the individual assemblies or units, so that the collation of these particular parts becomes a specific scheduling exercise in itself. Under these special circumstances, the project manager's office can provide help to the purchasing and production departments by collating all the parts requirements, and appraising departments of their actual commitments on a programmed basis. The various forms which this help can take will be more clearly understood if we analyse a very simple project and then deliberately complicate the delivery schedule.

In Figure 5.10 there is an exploded view of a two-drawer filing cabinet. Suppose, in the first instance, that only one cabinet is to be constructed. The simple parts list of Figure 5.11 would be adequate for production control purposes. Armed with this list, the production control clerks would be able to order all materials necessary for the construction of the single cabinet, whether they were to be bought-out or made in the factory. There need be no ambiguity at all about the total quantities necessary, or when they must be available. If one item has a very long lead time, this will determine the overall lead time for assembling the final kit of parts.

The raw materials, including items such as sheet metal and paint, would be specified on the actual manufacturing drawings in this case, although practice in this respect varies greatly from one company to another. Often, these materials are left to the production department to supply from common stock, according to the amounts which can be estimated from the drawings. The production engineer might write the quantities needed, allowing for wastage, on to route cards so that the correct amounts of raw materials could be withdrawn from stores. Unless larger quantities were to be consumed, there need be no attempt at special order activity for these items of common stock, since the replenishment of stocks would be triggered automatically from stock control records when a predetermined minimum level was reached for each stock item. Stock control, since it is not part of the scheduling process, is dealt with in Chapter 6, and will be ignored for the remainder of this discussion.

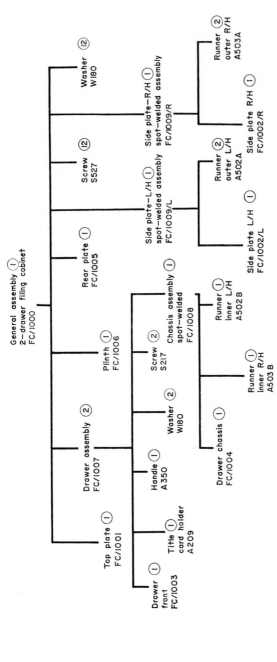

FIGURE 5.12 FILING CABINET FAMILY TREE
A family tree shows the arrangement into subassemblies
necessary to facilitate economic production

97

ITEM NO	PART NUMBER	DESCRIPTION	QTY	REMARKS
IA	FC/1007	Drawer assembly	2	
2A	FC/1009/L	Side plate welded assy L/H	I	
3A	FC/1009/R	Side plate welded assy R/H	I	
4	FC/1001	Top plate	I	
5	FC/1006	Plinth	I	
6	FC/1005	Rear plate	I	
7	S 527	Screw, self tapping	12	Acme Screw Company Type 1003ST−X
8	W 180	Washer, shakeproof	12	Acme Screw Company Type 459 SP

Iss	Mod No	Date	Sig	Iss	Mod No	Date	Sig	Iss	Mod No	Date	Sig
I	First	6−5−68									

Drawn by EFP	Checked AJP	Approved D L Lock	Date 1−5−68	

ROBINSON'S OFFICE FURNITURE COMPANY LIMITED, BIRMINGHAM

Title General assembly. Filing cabinet − Elite series − without lock, 2 drawer version	Sheet I of I sheets	Assembly number FC/1000

FIGURE 5.13 FILING CABINET GENERAL ASSEMBLY
Parts list arranged in family tree format

98

ITEM NO	PART NUMBER	DESCRIPTION	QTY	REMARKS
IA	FC/1008	Chassis assembly, welded	I	
2	A 209	Title card holder	I	Carter & Coy Ltd
3	A 350	Handle	I	Epsom & Salt Ltd
4	S 217	Screw	2	Acme Screw Company Type 347M−F
5	W 180	Washer, shakeproof	2	Acme Screw Company Type 459SP
6	FC/1003	Drawer front	I	

Iss	Mod No	Date	Sig	Iss	Mod No	Date	Sig	Iss	Mod No	Date	Sig
I	First	6−5−68									

Drawn by EFP	Checked AJP	Approved *DL Lock*	Date 31−4−68	

ROBINSON'S OFFICE FURNITURE COMPANY LIMITED, BIRMINGHAM

Title Drawer assembly	Sheet I of I sheets	Assembly number FC/1007

FIGURE 5.14 FILING CABINET DRAWER ASSEMBLY
Parts list

ITEM NO	PART NUMBER	DESCRIPTION	QTY	REMARKS
1	FC/1004	Drawer chassis	1	
2	A 503 B	Runner, inner, R/H	1	Smiths Ltd
3	A 502 B	Runner, inner, L/H	1	Smiths Ltd

Iss	Mod No	Date	Sig	Iss	Mod No	Date	Sig	Iss	Mod No	Date	Sig
1	First	6−5−68									

Drawn by EFP	Checked AJP	Approved *DL Lock*	Date 31−4−68	

ROBINSON'S OFFICE FURNITURE COMPANY LIMITED, BIRMINGHAM

Title Drawer chassis assembly, welded	Sheet 1 of 1 sheets	Assembly number FC/1008

FIGURE 5.15 FILING CABINET DRAWER CHASSIS
Parts list for welded assembly

ITEM NO	PART NUMBER	DESCRIPTION	QTY	REMARKS
1	FC/1002/L	Side plate L/H	1	
2	A 502 A	Runner, Outer, L/H	2	Smiths Ltd

Iss	Mod No	Date	Sig	Iss	Mod No	Date	Sig	Iss	Mod No	Date	Sig
1	First	6–5–68									

Drawn by EFP	Checked AJP	Approved *DL Lock*	Date 31–4–68	

ROBINSON'S OFFICE FURNITURE COMPANY LIMITED, BIRMINGHAM

Title Side plate welded assy L/H	Sheet I of I sheets	Assembly number FC/1009/L

FIGURE 5.16 FILING CABINET LEFT SIDE PLATE
Parts list

ITEM NO	PART NUMBER	DESCRIPTION	QTY	REMARKS
1	FC/1002/R	Side plate R/H	1	
2	A 503 A	Runner, outer, R/H	2	Smiths Ltd

Iss	Mod No	Date	Sig	Iss	Mod No	Date	Sig	Iss	Mod No	Date	Sig
1	First	6-5-68									

Drawn by EFP	Checked AJP	Approved *D.L.Lock*	Date 31-4-68	

ROBINSON'S OFFICE FURNITURE COMPANY LIMITED, BIRMINGHAM

Title Side plate welded assy R/H	Sheet 1 of 1 sheets	Assembly number FC/1009/R

FIGURE 5.17   FILING CABINET RIGHT SIDE PLATE
Parts list

STOCK COLLATION CARD							
USED ON ASSEMBLY OR MOD NO	PER ASSY	NO OF ASSY'S	TOTAL QTY	USED ON ASSEMBLY OR MOD NO	PER ASSY	NO OF ASSY's	TOTAL QTY
				TOTAL B/F	/////	/////	
TOTAL C/F	/////	/////					
Description					Part number		

FIGURE 5.18   STOCK COLLATION CARD
Suitable for one complex project

If, instead of just one filing cabinet, there is a need to produce several cabinets for a stock batch, or for delivery to a customer against one larger order, economies in labour times would be sought by loading the work in fairly large batches. The production engineer would take steps to break the assembly and manufacture down into a series of operations, so that each machine or jig used in the work need only be set up once. The final work breakdown might look something like that shown in the family tree in Figure 5.12.

Anticipating this type of subassembly breakdown, the drawing office would probably produce their parts lists according to the same breakdown in order that kits of parts could be marshalled in the stores for each of the particular production stages. The revised arrangement of parts lists, corresponding to the family tree of Figure 5.12, is included in full and ranges from the general assembly of Figure 5.13 to the smallest subassemblies in Figures 5.16 and 5.17.

Whilst the arrangement of parts lists in family tree order is very useful for manufacturing purposes, it is not so convenient for the purchasing of parts, or for the scheduling of manufacture for parts common to more than one assembly. In this particular example, there is only one common part, the washer, part number W180.

103

USAGE REASON → Main assy																	Spares & accessories	Total annual usage
Annual usage																		
↓ Part number ↓	Qty per / Total	Qty per / Total	Qty per / Total	Qty per / Total	Qty per / Total	Qty per / Total	Qty per / Total	Qty per / Total	Qty per / Total	Qty per / Total	Qty per / Total	Qty per / Total	Qty per / Total	Qty per / Total	Qty per / Total	Qty per / Total		

FIGURE 5.19 STOCK COLLATION CARD
Intended for multi-project use

Notice that this item appears twice on the simple parts list of Figure 5.11, where it is a fairly simple matter to add up the quantities to find the total requirement of washers. On the family tree, however, and on the corresponding parts lists, the washer appears in two different places, and only in the quantities necessary to make one of each respective assembly or subassembly. Some multiplication is necessary to arrive at the total quantity needed to make one main assembly.

One way of coping with this problem is to provide a card index. The cards are arranged in part-number sequence, and it helps if they can be accommodated in trays with their edges overlapping, so that the index marks are visible. A suitable card layout is shown at Figure 5.18. The work involves nothing less than the transferring of every item from the parts lists on to these cards, but it can be entrusted to typists or to other clerical staff. The parts lists are scanned systematically and common parts are brought to light by the existence of more than one entry on any card. Provision is made for the inclusion of modifications and the relevant modification numbers can be recorded against each change.

The amount of work in setting up a parts index may be so large that a contractor will shy away from the expense and effort. There are occasions, however, when this exercise must be carried out, and it may prove more costly in terms of time lost through materials shortages not to undertake the work in the first place. Once the index has been constructed, it can also be used for progress purposes, using coloured flags or signals on the card edges to show the current order status.

An extension of the common-parts scheduling and collation problem is encountered when more than one project is being undertaken at the same time, especially where assemblies used on one project are also required for some of the others. The modular operating theatres mentioned at the end of Chapter 4 provided a classic example of this particular difficulty. The projects varied in the sizes of theatres supplied, but the basic building elements were common to all types. The form shown in Figure 5.19 was used to overcome the problem and enabled stock levels to be set up on an estimated annual usage for every major assembly. Naturally, for smaller components, such as screws, nuts, and so on, normal stock control methods were sufficient, using a maximum-minimum reorder level. For large items such as door-frames, wall-panels, and expensive wall-mounted equipment, the collation lists proved invaluable in the control of inventory.

PARTS SCHEDULING BY THE LINE OF BALANCE TECHNIQUE

There remains one further aspect of parts scheduling which can affect project work and give rise to difficulties. Suppose that a number of identical units have to be produced according to some imposed timescale which does not allow manufacture to take place either in one complete batch or at a constant flow rate. The fact that lead times and the total quantities required will vary from one item to another means that it may not be a simple matter to determine just how many of any one part should be completed or in progress at a given time. The filing cabinet project will illustrate the problem, and can be used to demonstrate the line of balance technique.

Line of balance is basically a method for scheduling and displaying the progress of repetitive manufacturing programmes, although variants of the system have been developed for controlling a wide variety of other project activities. In common with PERT and CPA the technique had to make a journey across the Atlantic Ocean before becoming available to British managers. The age of the method is variously described by different authorities, so that the origin is given in one case as "in the 1950s" and in another as "before the Second World War."

Assume that an office furniture company has received a series of special orders for their two-drawer filing cabinets, type FC/1000, and that these are to be produced as "specials," according to delivery commitments. There is no possibility of completing them all as one single batch, because there is insufficient production capacity and space. The total quantity to be made will be about sixty, and orders totalling fifty cabinets have already been received for delivery at the rate shown in the following table –

DATE PROMISED	CUSTOMER	QUANTITY	CUMULATIVE QUANTITY
7 October 1968	Jones	5	5
11 October 1968	Jenkins	5	10
29 October 1968	Brown	10	20
4 November 1968	Williams	10	30
14 November 1968	Williams	10	40
26 November 1968	Parker	5	45
2 December 1968	Jenkins	5	50

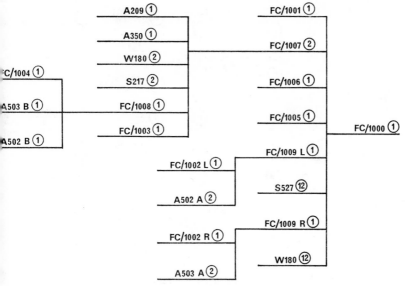

FIGURE 5.20 REDRAWN FILING CABINET FAMILY TREE
The revised arrangement is necessary to allow calculation
of lead times for a line of balance

The first step in the preparation of a line of balance calculation it
to obtain a family tree for the parts build-up. In the filing cabines
project this family tree already exists, as shown at Figure 5.12, but
it is convenient to redraw the tree laterally, so that the assembly
sequence runs from left to right. The revised family tree is shown
in Figure 5.20. The horizontal format is better suited to the addition
of timescale, for which the tree has to be further adapted by the
addition of event circles, as depicted in Figure 5.21. By now, the
family tree is beginning to look rather similar to a network diagram,
and indeed there is a considerable degree of correlation.

The numbers written in the small circles which appear alongside
each part number show the quantity of that particular part which
must be provided in order to construct one of the assemblies on which
it is to be used. This quantity will, therefore, be the same as that
shown on the parts list for the relevant assembly or subassembly.
In order to arrive at the total quantity of any item needed to complete one filing cabinet, it is necessary to multiply the quantities in
sequence along each path, from left to right. Thus, for example,

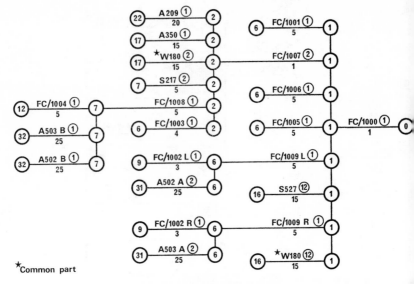

*Common part

FIGURE 5.21 CALCULATION OF LEAD TIMES FOR FILING
CABINET PARTS
An essential step in the preparation of a line of balance.
This chart enables the total lead time for each part or
assembly to be calculated

one A503B is needed to make one FC/1008, one FC/5008 is contained
in each FC/1007, but two FC/1007s are used for every FC/1000. The
total quantity of A503Bs is therefore $1 \times 1 \times 2$ for every complete
filing cabinet.

To calculate the total lead time for every part, the duration is
first estimated for each item individually, and written on to the family
tree as shown. In this case the durations have been written below the
lines, although this is only one of a wide number of variations, since
there is no standard notation for the method. By adding up the lead
times backwards, working from right to left along each path, the
total lead time for any event can be found. These results have been
written into the event circles in this example, and the times are
expressed in working days. All figures have been rounded up to the
nearest whole day, and time needed for kitting or machine setting
has been included. Each event denotes the completion of procurement or manufacture for the preceding part and the corresponding
start for the following item.

108

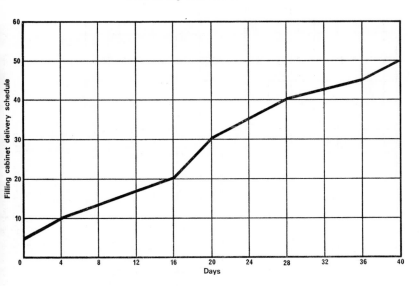

FIGURE 5.22 FILING CABINET DELIVERY COMMITMENT
All orders have been plotted cumulatively so that the graph
indicates the total number of cabinets which must have
been manufactured at any time

The family tree, as set up and annotated in Figure 5.21, tells us all we need to know about the provision of parts for one complete filing cabinet. Again taking part A503B as an example, we now know that two of these must be provided, and that they must be ordered at least thirty-two days before the filing cabinet is wanted. If they are not actually received by the seventh day before completion is due, the programme will run late. Notice that unlike a usual network, everything on this family tree is "critical." No leeway is allowed.

If, instead of just one filing cabinet, a batch of twenty had to be manufactured, the family tree could still be employed to determine the quantity/time relationships for all the constituent parts and assemblies. The planner would only have to carry out the calculation of results for a single cabinet, and then multiply all the quantities by twenty. The lead times in every case would be unaltered, provided that sufficient production capacity existed.

Before a series of repetitive batches can be considered, it is necessary to construct one more chart. This time, the delivery programme has to be drawn up on a graph, showing cumulative

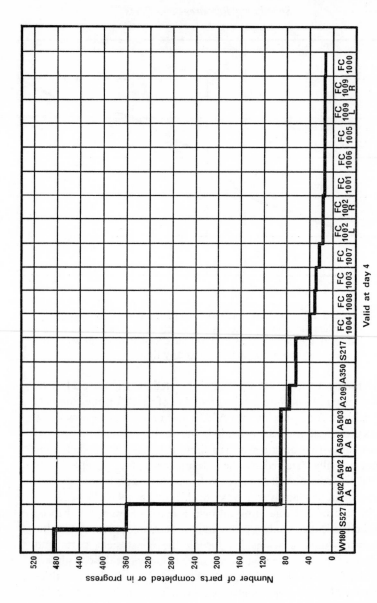

FIGURE 5.23 LINE OF BALANCE FOR FILING CABINET PARTS
A line of balance is only valid for one point in time. This
chart has been calculated for day 4 of the delivery schedule

deliveries against timescale. The result for the filing cabinet project is shown in Figure 5.22, where only working weekdays have been allowed as time available and the delivery commitments of the table on page 106 have been observed.

Suppose that day 4 of the delivery schedule has been reached and that the current status of all production has to be checked against the known delivery commitments. Taking the drawer runner, part number A503B, once again as an example, the lead time is known to be thirty-two days, and two of these runners must be provided for every filing cabinet. By projecting forward along the delivery graph from day 4 by the lead time of thirty-two days, day 36 is reached. By that time, forty-five cabinets must have been delivered. This means that at day 4, all the runners necessary to make forty-five cabinets must have been ordered or obtained. In other words, ninety parts number A503B must be on order.

Not only is it possible to calculate just how many parts should be on order at any given time but it is also possible to work out the quantities which must be actually available in stock. This is done by considering the end event in each case instead of the start event. In the case of the drawer runners, A503B, the result for day 4 would be based on a lead time of seven days, taking the projection on the delivery graph up to day 11. By allowing the same process as before, it is found that sufficient stock must be in hand at day 4 to complete sixteen cabinets.

If the calculation were to be repeated for all parts and assemblies used on the filing cabinet project, the result for day 4 of the programme would be that set out in the table overleaf. Only the start events have been considered for each part, in order to keep the example as simple as possible. This means that the quantities stated include all items which must be on order, in production, and completely finished.

Now refer to Figure 5.23, where the data accumulated on page 111 have been converted into chart form. Each separate item has been allocated a column to itself. The minimum quantity of parts which must be in progress or finished by day 4 if the programme is to be achieved is shown in each case by a horizontal line drawn across the columns. These quantities are called the "balance quantities," and the histogram type of curve which they form is the "line of balance." Remember that this result is only valid for the point in time at which the quantities were calculated, or day 4 of the project.

If the actual progress achieved at day 4 is plotted on the same

111

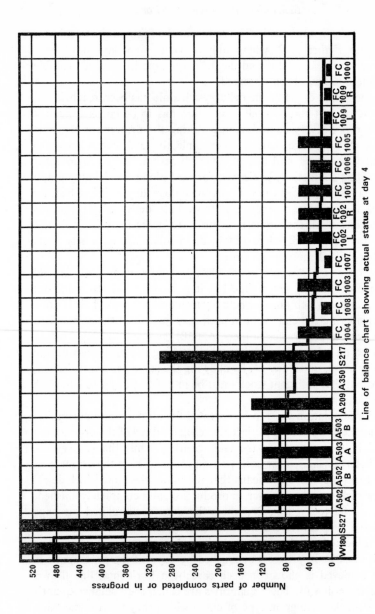

Line of balance chart showing actual status at day 4

FIGURE 5.24 FILING CABINET PROJECT
Line of balance completed to show actual status of project
at day 4 of the delivery schedule

112

PART NUMBER	QUANTITY (1 CABINET)	TOTAL LEAD TIME (DAYS)	NUMBER OF CABINETS	TOTAL QUANTITY
W180	4	17	31	} 484
W180	12	16	30	
S527	12	16	30	360
A502A	2	31	45	90
A502B	2	32	45	90
A503A	2	31	45	90
A503B	2	32	45	90
A209	2	22	38	76
A350	2	17	31	62
S217	4	7	16	64
FC/1004	2	12	20	40
FC/1008	2	7	16	32
FC/1003	2	6	15	30
FC/1007	2	2	12	24
FC/1002L	1	9	18	18
FC/1002R	1	9	18	18
FC/1001	1	6	15	15
FC/1006	1	6	15	15
FC/1005	1	6	15	15
FC/1009L	1	6	15	15
FC/1009R	1	6	15	15
FC/1000	1	1	11	11

CALCULATION OF BALANCE QUANTITIES

(Filing project at day 4)

chart, a display of the type shown in Figure 5.24 will materialise. The fruits of all these planning labours now become obvious, since it is clearly seen that any achievement which falls below the line of balance represents a failure to meet the programme.

In this particular example, parts W180, S527 and S217 have been bought out in quantities sufficient to meet the entire programme, as they are inexpensive. Part A350 is under the required level, which in this chart means that the order quantity was too small. The fact that forty have been ordered does not mean that forty have been received. In order to display this further information, the chart would have to be extended to include completion stages as well as start stages.

In fact, it is possible, although very laborious, to split up the family tree not only into separate parts and assemblies, but also into the different manufacturing operation stages which are necessary to produce each part. These operations, which might include fabrication, spraying, inspection, and the like, are all allotted columns on the final line of balance chart. If this is done, a very informative

113

display can be produced, but it is a high price to pay for a chart which is only valid for one day. The use of a computer becomes almost mandatory in these circumstances, both to cope with the volume of calculation and to minimise the risk of error.

Some companies achieve a satisfactory compromise in the use of line of balance by taking into account only those items which, from previous experience, are known to represent potential sources of danger to the delivery programme. One major aircraft company for example, adopting this approach, uses line of balance for controlling the scheduling of some parts for electronic assemblies but restricts application to the printed circuit subassemblies only, because they are known to be prone to delay.

The vertical scale can prove troublesome because of the wide range of quantities which might have to be accommodated. This has been true to a large extent in the filing cabinet example. Those items which appear to the right side of the chart have been drawn to a scale which does not allow sufficient accuracy, whilst those on the left side overshoot the top margin. A logarithmic scale would have been necessary to overcome this particular problem.

The other shortcomings which are demonstrated by the line of balance chart of Figure 5.24 stem from the spot welded assemblies. They could have originated from a breakdown of the spot welding machine. If a machine breakdown did occur, there would be no need to draw a line of balance chart to indicate that trouble of some sort was in store. The chart would be necessary, however, to display the true extent of the problem. The biggest advantage of the line of balance technique is that it provides a visual display which highlights the problem areas. As such, the charts can be shown to higher executives at project meetings, where they save time by satisfying the principle of management by exception.

6

MATERIALS CONTROL

"Give us the tools and we'll finish the job!" was a familiar wartime slogan. Substitute "materials" for "tools" and this entreaty can be borrowed for project management, with none of the original truth being lost. If the raw materials or components for any part of a project are not available for use at the right time in the correct quantities and condition, the programme may be delayed beyond redemption.

When delays are caused by material shortages, one can always expect an increase in project costs. There is the obvious fact that some workers may simply be unable to carry on with their work until the shortages have been made good. Their wages continue to be paid during the idle period, charged to "idle" or "waiting" time, and as such will be a dead loss against profit. Even if the workers can be found other temporary fill-in jobs, disruption in the smooth flow of project activity will cause estimates of man-hours to be overspent.

It is too much to expect that shortages will never arise, even in the best managed undertaking. Sometimes last minute demands are made on a purchasing department as a result of additions or changes to the project requirements. The usual cause of shortages, however, especially when they occur in considerable numbers, can be attributed to a failure in some part of the contractor's organisation. When deficiencies arise, urgent measures must be put in hand to obtain the missing goods. Such crash actions can be limited to essential cases by the intelligent application of CPA techniques, but all too often desperate deeds will be necessary.

It is an unfortunate fact that material lead times frequently extend to several months under normal circumstances and it follows that these procurement activities stand a good chance of being found included along the critical path on the PERT network. Whenever crash actions are applied, increased costs can be expected to result from two possible causes. If immediate delivery of an item is required, this becomes the all-important factor in choosing a supplier and purchasing price is relegated to second consideration. The contractor may be forced to buy from a very expensive supplier simply because he is the only firm able to supply from stock. Purchasing expenses will also be greater when extreme urgency is being applied. Time will be taken up in many additional telephone calls and transport costs may be higher because express carriage or air freight charges must be paid. Goods imported from overseas are sometimes especially costly to obtain at short notice.

Shortages of materials can prove serious, even where the resulting delays do not extend the overall delivery date of the project. Apart from the effects already mentioned on individual job times and material costs, there is a risk that production morale will be damaged. Teamwork, and the unbridled co-operation of all project participants is really essential to the economic and efficient progress of the work. Should many jobs become delayed or stopped as a result of shortages, this will be interpreted as a failure on the part of the management, by those on the shop floor. Idle people are not happy people and discontent will be bred. Why should the shop-floor personnel put themselves out to rectify a mess which the management has caused? Generation of a good team spirit is a useful way of helping a project along, and materials control can make a contribution to achieving or defeating this end.

Perhaps a good way to emphasise the importance of materials control is to remember that on a typical project more than half the total expenditure may be attributed to the usage of materials. Competitive buying, therefore, has major significance with regard to the overall project profits, whilst any overspending on material budgets will have an appreciable effect in reducing the end profit. Another aspect of the relatively high cost of project materials is bound up with the question of capital investment. If the materials are bought before they are required, money is tied up in an unprofitable way and may attract bank charges if the firm has an overdraft.

Contracts which include an enforceable penalty clause will suffer a reduction in profit from a delay in delivery. Another effect of late completion is that the project billing will be held up. This means that the contractor is forced to bear the cost of investment for a longer period than he had planned. From any angle, a late delivery is a bad thing. The customer is dissatisfied and profits are down or non-existent. If material shortages produce delays, the burden of guilt lies heavily on the shoulders of those who allowed them to occur.

Thus the control of materials can influence potential profits in many ways, both directly and indirectly. There are also other considerations, which will be mentioned later, concerning features such as storage and quality. One of the prerequisites for the successful and profitable completion of any project is, therefore, a competent purchasing department. Before moving on to discuss some aspects of materials control in greater detail, it is best to outline the salient responsibilities of that department.

THE PURCHASING CYCLE

Some people regard a purchasing department as an office staffed by individuals whose only function in commercial life is to copy-type purchase orders and then pop them into the post. Unfortunately this conception may sometimes approach too near to the truth for comfort. If indeed this ever turned out to be the case any attempt at materials control would be condemned to death before birth. The normal sequence of events leading to the receipt of goods into stores can be illustrated by considering the purchasing cycle in Figure 6.1, which is not unlike the project cycle of Chapter 1. In fact, procurement of any item could be regarded as a mini-project in itself. The project manager is replaced in this analogy by the purchasing manager, around whom all buying activities revolve.

The purchasing cycle is activated by the discovery of a need for raw materials or components. The origin of this discovery may lie in stock control, stores, engineering, or production control, depending on the type of goods and the organisation of the firm. Once the need has been recognised, action will be started by an application to the company's buyer. The application will usually be conveyed on a written requisition, possibly requiring some form of authorisation to allow expenditure of the money involved.

The first responsibility of the buyer will be to select a suitable

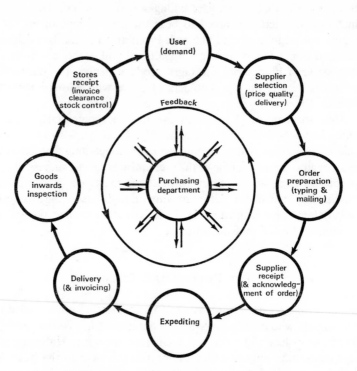

FIGURE 6.1 THE PURCHASING CYCLE
Each purchase order is a mini project. Compare this chart
with the project cycle shown in Figure 1.2

source of supply. Occasionally, only one supplier can be chosen and
he may be specified on the requisition. Limitation of choice usually
arises when the goods are highly specialised. Even so, for goods which
are only manufactured by one firm, there may be a choice between
different stockists. In all other cases, the supplier must be chosen
after a process involving the collection of several competitive quotations. One would normally expect the buyer to select the lowest
priced quotation consistent with delivery time and quality.

Moving one more step round the cycle, the order has to be type-
written and put into the hands of the supplier, by way of the postal
system. This is the most routine, obvious, and apparently irrelevant
part of the purchasing cycle. What has this to do with project
management? The answer lies in the time taken. Several days of

valuable project time can be consumed, even by this mundane and simple activity. Procurement lead times on the PERT network must always allow for such delays. In fact, unless emergency measures are contemplated, two weeks should always be regarded as a minimum purchase lead time, even for ex-stock quotations.

When the chosen supplier has received his order, he will be expected to return an acknowledgement confirming the broad details of price and delivery. Naturally these details must be compared to the original quotation, and the buyer will jump into action if there is any discrepancy. As far as the purchaser is concerned, the period which follows will be one of waiting, and a great deal of reliance will have to be placed on the ability of the supplier to meet his obligations. That is not to say that the purchaser can do nothing. This is the time when the company's expeditor can earn his money by keeping the supplier reminded of his obligations. Expediting also provides an early warning system, soliciting advance notice of any difficulties which the supplier might encounter.

Receipt of the goods is not the end of the story. The consignment must be examined by the goods inwards inspectors to find out if any damage has occurred in transit. There may also have been some mistake, either in the quantity supplied or in the nature of the goods. If the articles were received according to the exact order specification, the goods inwards department will circulate copies of a goods inwards certificate. One copy of the certificate will go to the accounts department who need it before they can allow payment of the supplier's invoice. Another copy will go to the buying department, cutting short any further expediting action and closing the books on that particular order. Routing of other copies depends on the nature of the firm, and the goods, and is not relevant here.

If the consignment is not received in a satisfactory condition for any reason, it will be sent smartly back whence it came, accompanied by a goods inwards reject note. Circulation of the reject note generally follows that of the acceptance certificates but it will produce the opposite reactions from the various recipients. The accounts department, for instance, would certainly not allow payment of the invoice, whilst the expeditor would redouble his efforts instead of closing his book.

When the correct articles have been received, they will be passed into stores, to await withdrawal for actual use. At the same time the stock records must be up-dated to show the addition of the new arrivals into stock holding. If the consignment was ordered for repeating production stocks, there will be a gradual depletion as usage takes place, until the stock records indicate a reorder need. Then the whole purchasing cycle is set in motion once more.

Specifying the Purchase Order

The purchase of an item has already been referred to as a "mini-project." It follows that just as a project needs to be provided with a complete specification, so does a purchase order. There are three main essentials for this particular type of specification. These are budgeted price, delivery date, and a complete description of the goods. If the originator of a purchase requisition does not supply all these details he cannot reasonably be surprised if his purchasing department appears to let him down. Specifications of price and delivery are straightforward enough. The price limit can be set either by reference to the project budgets or by a knowledge of the market. The delivery date will be thrown out from the project PERT control network. A full description of the goods may, however, give rise to slightly more difficulty and later misunderstandings.

Parts or materials can usually be specified by reference to a manufacturer's catalogue number or part number. This would appear to be a sufficiently rigid description of the goods but it must be remembered that some suppliers reserve the right to change their designs without notice. Such a change could be quite slight, and insignificant to the majority of users, whilst rendering the product utterly useless for the project for which it was intended. An example of this would be provided by a manufacturer who changed the material of a component. The catalogue description and illustration might look identical for both versions of the item but the strength, weight, and other physical properties would all change.

The Importance of Correct Specification. Sometimes a British Standards Specification exists which can be used to specify the exact requirements. There are also many specifications provided by other official bodies, including those for the requirements of the three armed forces. Many companies provide their own drawings and specifications and allocate part numbers themselves. The drawings in such cases will show all the critical features of the products and a copy of the drawing would accompany each purchase order. This practice costs a considerable amount of drawing office time but has much to commend it. Apart from removal of ambiguities in the requirements of each purchase order, provision is made for a common part-numbering system which simplifies all stock handling and purchasing procedures and eases the burden of the cost office.

An example from my own experience should help to emphasise the pitfalls of inadequate purchase specifications. A standard product had been in production for several years without any significant design change. The apparatus was for use in operating theatres and required the fitting of three special taps. These taps were of the elbow-lever action type, which enabled the surgeon to move the levers from on to off without contaminating his gloved hands. Each tap was provided with a threaded hose outlet connection. The direction of rotation of the lever, and the positions which it occupied at both the on and off positions were critical to the correct assembly and operation of the equipment.

Taps were carried in the general stores as a standard stock item but the rate of usage was very low. Reorder quantities were always small and each time an order was placed the taps had to be manufactured specially by the supplier. No drawing existed but the supply of taps never gave any trouble since the supplier always remembered the design from previous orders. An occasion then arose when the usual manufacturer fell down very badly on delivery and, as stocks had run out, alternative sources were sought. From this time onwards a number of different firms were approached to supply taps. Each time a purchase order was sent a written account of the requirements was included, but there were still no drawings.

Every conceivable error arose in the subsequent supply of these items. Taps were sometimes received with the wrong type of hose connections or without any hose connection at all. At other times the levers were supplied as "wrist action" instead of "elbow lever," these being different in shape and length. On one occasion taps were found to have the wrong direction of rotation, being anti-clockwise for off instead of clockwise. An error of ninety degrees in the lever positions at on and off happened with one batch. Sometimes the taps were accepted into stock without the errors being discovered until they were required for use.

Eventually, a drawing of an ideal tap was produced. This gave outline dimensions, the general shape, details of the hose connections, and an accurate definition of the lever action. Every time a fresh order was placed, one copy of the drawing accompanied the order, whilst a second was sent to the goods inwards inspectors to enable a complete check of the items to be made on receipt. Very few mistakes occurred subsequently, and when they did, the goods inwards inspectors were able to spot them immediately and arrange for the defects to be put right by the supplier. The improvement was dramatic, immediate, and permanent. All the previous trouble could have been prevented if only the correct procedure had been followed all along.

ORDERING TO A PLAN

It is clear that if materials are not ordered in sufficient time, shortages may result on the production floor. Whilst late ordering can bring serious consequences, there are often reasons why purchases should not be made too early in a programme. Materials ordered so that they arrive long before they are required will have to be paid for earlier than is necessary. Problems of storage may result from premature deliveries of bulky items. As a general rule, however, shortages will always provide the major headaches. Any decision to delay the issue of purchasing instructions must be tempered with caution and adequate time should be allowed for unforeseen contingencies. What would happen if an important consignment arrived on the very day it was required for use only to be rejected by the goods inwards inspectors as unfit?

There are methods for ensuring that items will be available on the required date but without the need to accept very early deliveries or premature invoices from suppliers. Possibly the best way is to pre-warn all the suppliers of the intention to purchase. This can be taken to the extent of actually issuing the purchase orders as soon as the requirement becomes known, but writing specific instructions on to each order to the effect that delivery will not be needed until a certain date. In some cases, for instance where very large quantities of parts are involved, deliveries can be scheduled in batches, to take place over quite a long period at an agreed rate. Of course the suppliers must be willing to accept conditions of this nature, but the practice is widely used. The method is often referred to as a "call-off" procedure, the stocks being "called off" as and when they are actually needed. The supplier can either store the balance of each order himself, or manufacture according to a corresponding schedule.

At first sight, it may appear that these considerations will apply more to those firms engaged on mass production rather than to single projects. Some of the bigger projects do, however, consume large quantities of materials. For instance, one would hardly consider the building of a large office block as mass production but enormous quantities of building supplies may nevertheless be involved. There would be very obvious difficulties if, say, all the supplies were delivered before work had begun on site clearance. Chaos would result, with the whole area strewn with bags of cement, sand, ballast, and bricks. Access for clearance would then be impossible and some of the supplies would have to be found accommodation elsewhere or removed altogether – at considerable extra expense.

In the case of the bricks, or the sand and ballast, the difficulties presented by early delivery would be mainly those of storage. Consider instead a project for the construction of one special electronic computer. 10 000 transistors will be needed to complete the job, and they are going to cost an average of £0.25 (5 shillings) each. This will involve an investment of £2500, an appreciable sum of money by any standards. All of these components could be stored in a very small space so that early delivery would present no problem in that area. But could 10 000 transistors all be used on a single project within a few days after receipt? It would obviously be unwise to commit all this expenditure too early in the project. Far better to arrange for deliveries in scheduled batches, spread over a period corresponding to the estimated rate of usage. The contractor will almost certainly be able to reap the advantage of price concessions associated with such large quantities but he will not be asked to pay until the components are actually required for use.

Between the two extremes of flow production and manufacture of single units there exists a wide range of projects where production must take place on a basis of repeating single units, or in batches of several units at a time. Preparation of ordering schedules for this kind of work can become quite involved and techniques may include line of balance charts. An example of repetitive manufacture calling for this type of control would be provided by a series of similar projects, for different customers, all aimed at producing identical equipment but at different delivery dates. One could draw up a delivery schedule for the dispatch of all these identical units and prepare a line of balance chart accordingly.

Having established that ideally materials should be ordered to a project plan, there remain one or two questions concerning the common-sense application of that plan. Returning to the case of the custom-built computer, and the 10 000 transistors, there is no question that an order for these particular components should be arranged on a planned call-off basis if at all possible. But what about the inexpensive components, such as screws, nuts, washers, solder tags, and so on? It would be nonsensical to attempt ordering these items to any plan. Rather, one would see to it that the whole quantity was ordered in advance and with a generous supply to spare. Rigid control would not be necessary. The application of such control would cost more than the value of the materials themselves and might attract ridicule from the suppliers into the bargain. Some items will therefore be controlled from the project plan whilst others will not. Where is the line to be drawn?

The solution of this problem depends on the adoption of a common-sense approach to enable the materials to be classified into those items which require rigid control and those which do not. This classification will usually be decided after consideration of two factors: volume and value. Control will always be applied most rigorously to parts which involve the greatest investment of either storage space or money. In practice the choice is seldom difficult. On most projects, there will be one or two items which stand out like beacons as being big or expensive, or both. If the project is long-term and includes the production of large numbers of assemblies or subassemblies in repeating batches, materials will be controlled by methods more akin to normal production stock routines. Line of balance techniques may be used for the actual work plans, whilst stocks can be classified for control purposes using the ABC system.

Before moving on to take a closer look at the ABC system of materials control, it should be recognised that ordering to a plan on a short-term project is not likely to be one of the project manager's worries. He can expect to find himself far more fully occupied in trying to obtain his materials in an impossibly short space of time. It has already been noted that procurement lead times have a habit of falling on to the critical path. When slips occur early in a programme and no let-up of delivery time can be allowed, the remaining part of the work will resemble an incompressible object being squeezed between two irresistible forces. The procurement activity stands a high chance of being included within the squeeze, owing to the usual tendency of engineers to provide the ordering specifications too late.

The ABC System of Stock Control

Manufacturing firms which carry a wide range of stock items have at their disposal reliable methods for classifying materials into those which warrant rigid control and those which do not. One of these methods is the ABC system of stock control. Although primarily intended for production stocks, the system may prove useful to long-term projects which include sizeable production runs. It is possible for a single project to be so large that some parts have to be produced in quantities which demand mass production techniques. One example might be provided by a project to install street lighting along a stretch of motorway. Although only one project is involved, under the control of one network and one project manager, thousands of street lamps may have to be specially made. These lamps can be treated for all intents and purposes as production quantity items. Manufacture might be spread over several years and the associated materials could be handled from production stocks.

Two main objectives can be assigned to the stock controller. Adequate supplies of materials must be maintained to underwrite the continuity of production at all times. On the other hand, stock levels must not be allowed to build up into an excessive inventory investment. One measure of the effectiveness of stock control is the inventory turn rate. This is a ratio, being the number of times by which the average value of stock and work in progress can be divided into the total quantity of stocks sold each year. In other words, this is the number of times by which the stocks and work in progress are "turned over" in one complete year. In a light engineering firm, this ratio could be expected to lie between two and four, although it will vary according to the type of work. The ABC system is one way of ensuring that this objective will be achieved for the minimum expenditure of stock control effort.

Now picture the general stores of any industrial company of average size or larger. In our mind's eye we can see row upon row

125

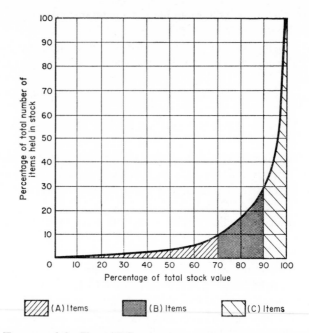

FIGURE 6.2 THE ABC METHOD OF STOCK CONTROL
By concentrating stock control vigilance on the few most
expensive *A* items effective inventory reduction can be
achieved with minimum effort

and tier upon tier of racking, loaded with a great variety of different
parts. The items stocked will range from relatively inexpensive
screws, nuts, bolts, and so on, stocked in their thousands, to a smaller
number of much more expensive components. Under these normal
conditions there is a rule which can be applied with confidence
although the benefit of mathematical proof is lacking. This rule has
two complementary parts, the first of which states that 70 per cent
of the total stock value is vested in only 10 per cent of the physical
number of items held. The rule goes on to claim that 70 per cent of
the number of items held could be chosen to represent only 10 per
cent of the total stock value. The ABC stock-control system depends
upon the acceptance of this rule, or at least its general principle.

The derivation of the terms *A*, *B*, and *C* can be explained by reference to Figure 6.2, which is one way of representing the concept
graphically. The *A* items are those which add up to 70 per cent of

the total stock value. These will be controlled very carefully and ordering quantities kept as small as possible. It is also in the *A* area that most money can be saved by shopping around for lowest prices. At the other extreme, the *C* items require only the minimum of supervision, the real efforts being aimed at making sure that stocks do not run out. One method for controlling these low value parts is to keep them in two bins – the "two-bin method." One bin is kept in reserve and as soon as the first becomes exhausted, the second is brought into use. When the second bin sees the light of day it is recognised as the signal to reorder a further two bin's worth.

Another glance at the curve of Figure 7.2 will show that we are left with the inbetween *B* goods amounting to 20 per cent of the stock value, and 20 per cent of the number of items. These parts can be controlled from stock cards on a "max–min" basis. This means that the intervals between reordering will be arranged so that the stock level is allowed to fluctuate between predetermined maximum and minimum levels. The stock cards for these *B* parts may be filed with the *A* cards, which have a different background colour.

PURCHASE OF SMALL QUANTITIES

Purchase orders for small quantities of materials or components are often a specific feature of projects where the work is non-repetitive and confined to the completion of only one end product. In these cases the purchasing department will be faced with appreciable handicaps when they attempt to achieve short-term deliveries and low costs. A single small component may be vital to the success of a project. Although this component assumes very important dimensions in the eyes of the project manager, to the supplier it will be seen only for its nuisance value, yielding small profit and disrupting the flow of larger orders to more valuable customers.

If the contractor is a large company, or part of a big group, there is always a possibility that the supplier may give good service in the fond hope that larger follow-up orders will result. Although the supplier's optimism may be completely groundless it would be a very foolish purchasing or project manager who set out deliberately to discourage him. The same motives sometimes prompt suppliers to proffer free samples of their wares. Not only do items obtained in this way cost nothing but they can usually be procured by return of post, or out of a representative's brief case. Small stocks are sometimes reserved by suppliers for this very purpose, and if the formalities of paperwork and ordering procedures are circumvented, much valuable project time is saved. Project managers would obviously be ill-advised to consider planning a project on the basis of materials supplied from free samples, but it should be remembered that some projects have been given the kiss of life by items procured in this way after all other methods have been tried and found wanting.

Items ordered in very small quantities will usually cost the purchaser more money than they would if bought in larger amounts. The reasons for this cost/quantity relationship are well known and numerous. Some of them also apply to parts manufactured by the contractor's own production departments. They include longer machine set-up time compared to productive running time, higher tooling costs for each unit produced, and the absence of quantity discounts on the price of raw materials consumed. Long production runs enable the operatives to acquire dexterity and specialised job knowledge, whereas shorter runs reduce, or prohibit, any benefits which learning could have yielded. Other penalties of small quantity orders include higher costs per unit for packing, transport, documentation, and general handling. These are some of the factors which can compel suppliers to charge higher prices for very small purchases.

Quantity discounts offered by suppliers have been known to induce purchasers to buy beyond their immediate needs. Suppose, for example, that a particular project requires eight very expensive instruments. It is quite possible that the unit price for these devices could be quoted on a one to nine quantity basis. Orders for ten or more might result in a lower cost per instrument. In these circumstances the buyer might decide to buy ten, at the lower price, although only eight are required immediately. Any saving on unit cost, however, will not be worth the price of two surplus units left on the shelf after project completion. The only possible justification for buying above the net requirement would be to offset expected breakages (in which case a budget must exist) or against a *certain* follow-up customer order for spares. The project manager must be given the opportunity and power to veto inflated order quantities. Surplus stocks can accumulate with embarrassing speed if restraint is not exercised.

128

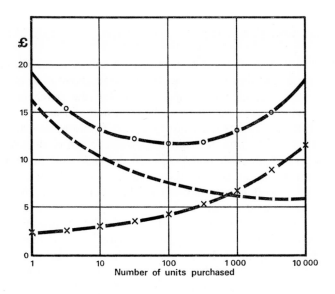

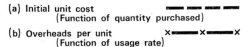

(a) Initial unit cost — — — —
    (Function of quantity purchased)

(b) Overheads per unit x——x——x
    (Function of usage rate)

(c) Total effective unit o——o——o
    (a + b)

FIGURE 6.3 ECONOMIC PURCHASE QUANTITY
Factors other than quantity discounts may determine the
most economic quantity to purchase at each reorder point

Stocks for continuous or batch production are also prone to
inflation from the lure of quantity discounts. Overstocking leads to a
reduced inventory turn ratio and increases investment compared to
profit. There will also be a greater risk of stock being made redundant
owing to design changes or discontinued products. Curves can be
drawn to show the relationship between purchased quantity, unit
cost, and the overhead costs attracted as a result of storage and investment. Figure 6.3 shows the appearance which one set of these
curves might take.

Curve (*a*) is the result of quantity discounts which increase as the
size of each order is extended. Beyond a certain number of items the
curve flattens out so that no further cost advantage can be achieved.
In fact, if truly enormous purchases are contemplated, they can

actually create a market shortage of the commodity which *increases* the unit cost. Fortunately, project managers are hardly likely to encounter this particular problem.

Curve (*b*) shows the cost of keeping each unit of stock. The curve does not start at zero but sets out from a fixed overhead level representing the cost of raising and progressing the purchase order documentation. The rise in costs for each unit will depend on the usage rate. We can assume, however, that as more units are purchased for a given rate of usage, the average length of storage time must increase for each unit. This will not only cost more space rental but will tie up additional capital. A point could be envisaged where the stockholding was expanded to a point where some of it would never be used at all.

Curve (*c*) is a composite result obtained by adding curves (*a*) and (*b*) together. This gives us the total real cost of buying and stocking each unit. The lowest point on this curve obviously shows the ideal quantity to purchase where cost is the only consideration. Production rate could be too low to justify orders of this size. On the other hand, larger orders may have to be placed in order to ensure continuity of production by the avoidance of shortages.

Expediting

First reliance on the procurement of goods in time to meet project requirements must be vested in the purchasing department. Once each order has been placed, responsibility shifts from the buyer to the expeditor, although in some smaller companies the buyer will double both roles. The function of expediting, contrary to popular belief, is not just a process for chasing up goods which are overdue for delivery. Rather, one should regard expediting as a routine procedure for monitoring the progress of each order. The aim is to ensure that scheduled deliveries will be achieved or to provide adequate warning of any impending delays.

One normal expediting method might consist of a simple arrangement of cards in a file, signalling some point in time for every individual order when a reminder to the supplier would seem propitious. As each reminder becomes due, a standard postcard can be dispatched, tactfully asking the supplier to confirm his original delivery promise. Obviously if this confirmation is not forthcoming, considerable activity will be generated within the purchasing department which will not abate until the supplier has been persuaded to change his mind.

The buyer may be able to locate an alternative source of supply. Sometimes a new method of approach to the original supplier can produce the desired result. An offer to arrange collection of goods from the supplier's premises, for instance, will make the supplier realise that the purchaser is willing to put himself out, and this should convince him that on this occasion at least there is a genuine urgency. Another possibility is sometimes provided by an approach to the design engineers for advice. They can often help by suggesting more readily available substitute components or materials.

A carefully composed letter, explaining the specific urgency of the problem and the vital nature of the project in relation to the nation's export drive, has been known to reduce a delivery promise from sixteen weeks to fourteen days. This particular achievement was all the more remarkable since the required item was a single flexible drive shaft, costing no more than £3, and manufactured as a "special." Similar letters were sent to two other suppliers with almost the same degree of success on other shortages for the project. A letter is perhaps becoming a rather unusual form of approach in these days of the telephone. Possibly the written word carries more weight than the spoken counterpart. A telephone call is soon forgotten but a letter is a tangible object which remains under the eye as a constant reminder.

If the supplier cannot deliver the goods on time in spite of pressure from the expediting department, the project manager must be brought into the picture. He can then decide just how important the delay is likely to be and authorise emergency measures if they are considered to be justified by project needs. In the last resort, the project manager must feel free to be able to take over the reins himself. A project manager should be motivated by a sense of personal involvement with the success of his contract.

The purchasing department will not usually be directing all their attention to one project, unless it is very big. Quite understandably, each purchase order could be regarded by the expediters as just another from the large number passing through their hands every day. Projects of sufficient size can justify the allocation of full-time expediting and buying clerks within the purchasing department and this can improve control.

To the project manager, however, any serious material shortage which threatens the success of his project may cause him to reflect on the progress of his own career. He will perhaps realise that his own fortunes can be closely linked to those of the project in his charge. This realisation should spur him on to exercise all his initiative, perseverance, tact, and (in the last resort) guile. For these reasons the project manager can sometimes be successful in clearing a shortage which has been declared by others to be inevitable. He refuses to accept defeat and explores every avenue until a solution can be found.

PROJECT PURCHASING VERSUS STOCK PURCHASING

Imagine a large factory churning out a wide range of products in quantity. Suppose also that all the materials required for production are supplied from one vast main store. One could foresee the possibility of a new project being completed entirely from the comprehensive range of stocks available with no need to buy any special parts. An unlikely possibility certainly, but one which could nevertheless arise where the special project was within the firm's customary line of business. Of course, the materials used in the project would have to be reordered at some time to make good the stocks used, but these replacement orders could be automatic, triggered by stock levels. Some obvious advantages can be accredited to this situation. There would be no need to purchase any materials in small quantities but rather one could keep to the normal routine of ordering in economic batch sizes. No special arrangements for project storage need be contemplated, although the project manager would be well advised to see that the stores reserved or "preallocated" the necessary materials.

Now to consider a very small company, so small in fact that virtually no production stocks at all are carried. Every time a new project appears on the scene, each single item must be painstakingly ordered, right down to the last nut, bolt, and washer. At first sight this example, a case of "project purchasing," seems even more improbable than the "stock purchasing" condition of the larger company. There are, however, some definite advantages to be gained from the adoption of a project purchasing policy, whether the company is large or small. Before moving on to discuss the more favourable aspects, one or two of the disadvantages must be described.

The most serious drawbacks of project purchasing occur when a company is running more than one project at a time, with separate purchasing for each. Any parts common to two or more of these contracts must be ordered and stored separately. Total purchases have to be split into smaller quantities with the result that quantity discounts are forfeit or reduced. Two separate stores occupy more floor area than one combined store with the same total capacity. If max–min level control is used in a production store, and common items are also kept in a project store, there is a tendency for the total stockholding to be increased, with a reduction in the inventory turn ratio. These are all serious disadvantages, not to be dismissed lightly. Why then should project purchasing ever be considered as a feasible system?

Two very good reasons exist for advocating project purchase and storage whenever this can be arranged. The first of these arises from a weakness inherent in most preallocation systems. The only safe method for preallocating stocks is to withdraw them from general stores and place them in a separate project store. If this is not done we can be certain that preallocation or not, some of the stock will be used on other work in a mysterious way and may not be available when most needed. Cheery assurances from the storekeeper that the deficient items are "on order" or "due in any day now" will not be well received. A project cannot be completed with promises.

The second advantage afforded by project purchasing over stock purchasing is bound up with the improved cost and budget analysis which it affords. This is illustrated in Figure 6.4 which compares cost data obtained by three different techniques. All the curves have one common property. Each has been drawn by adding together the material expenditure on a week-by-week basis as the project proceeds. Only the source of the cost information has been changed. Curve (*b*) is the only example which could be derived in all circumstances whether stock or contract purchasing had been adopted. In this case, material costs have been obtained by valuing the items listed on each stores requisition, following removal of the materials for use. Addition of all these requisition values will yield the cost of all project materials consumed at any time. Errors can arise owing to discrepancies between the quantities stated on the requisitions and the amounts actually issued. The valuations could also be inaccurate if outdated standard costs have been applied. One would not expect these errors to reach significant proportions, however, unless there

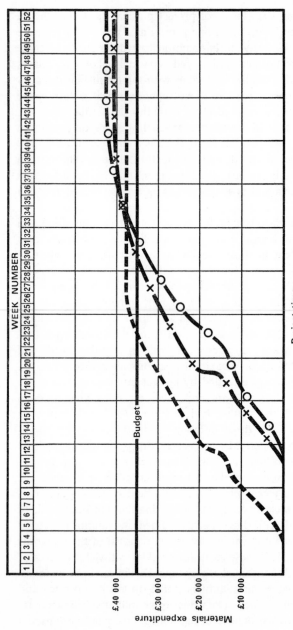

FIGURE 6.4 MONITORING MATERIAL COSTS

There are three basic ways in which material costs can be collected but the earliest
information is obtained by summing the value of purchase orders committed

134

were serious shortcomings in the administration of the stores or accounting functions. The real disadvantages of this most usual form of costing do not become apparent until the results are compared with those obtained from alternative methods.

Project purchasing, often called "contract purchasing," allows material costs to be picked up as each purchase order is issued. Plotting the records obtained in this way gives us a good indication of expenditure committed well in advance of the time when the materials will actually be consumed. Any items already available from normal production stocks, for which special purchase orders are not necessary, must of course be taken into account and included in the total commitment. This is easily accomplished. All that is necessary is to withdraw these materials from production stores in advance and preallocate them by transferring the amounts required into project stores. The requisitions used to withdraw these materials from the production stores can then be costed from standard cost data, and the costs added to the "committed" total.

Curve (*a*) of Figure 6.4 shows how data from committed materials expenditure can provide the earliest possible signal that budgets are in danger of being exceeded. Once again, discrepancies can be introduced if errors in valuation have occurred but, as before, these differences should be too small to destroy the validity of any trend indicated. Committed expenditure analysis is most useful for predicting the probable profitability which can be achieved, and for indicating any need for increased vigilance if budgets are threatened. The method is, however, of little use in measuring actual profit on project completion, for reasons which are demonstrated by curve (*c*).

Payments made against suppliers' invoices provide the basic and most accurate account of material purchase costs for a contract. Project purchasing is an essential condition otherwise invoices cannot be related to the specific project being costed. Curve (*c*) shows the way in which this type of cost information builds up with time. Note that this curve lags behind both the others by an appreciable period. Invoices will only be paid after goods have been received into stock. The usual office routines for invoice clearance must mean the elapse of a few more weeks before the cheques are signed. Suppliers do not always submit their invoices promptly and this can introduce further delays before payment is made for materials received. All these time lags provide free credit for the purchaser but retard the date when the final assessment of true project costs can be made. The significant fact which emerges here is that the information is far too late to allow any application for budget control purposes. By the time the facts are known, the money is already spent and nothing can be done. This emphasises the importance of keeping tabs on committed expenditure. None of this can be possible, however, unless project purchasing is adopted.

Before leaving Figure 6.4, observe that all three curves attain different final values. In this example the intervals have been purposely exaggerated, and in practice no more than about 5 per cent of the total material costs should separate the highest and lowest asymptotes. Curve (a), the sum of material costs committed, may not reach the true cost value owing to slight differences between suppliers quotations and their final invoices. Extra costs can arise when purchase orders are placed after quotation validities are time-expired. Other factors could include incidental expenses, such as freight, packing, insurance, and import duty costs. Withdrawals from stores, curve (b), did not add up to the true total project material cost, shown by curve (c). This could imply that some over-ordering took place, or that part of the project stocks were made redundant by design modifications. When surpluses are accumulated these must be accepted as a charge against profits unless they can be used elsewhere or returned to the suppliers for full credit, otherwise they will only have to be written off at a later date.

Some contracts for HM Government demand that items are purchased against certification of fitness for use. Even raw materials will be included, and the customer may arrange for samples to be tested in their own laboratories. One or other of the ministry inspectorates would be appointed to supervise and administer inspection routines, both on the contractor's own premises and at the establishments of at least some of the suppliers. As each consignment receives its inspection clearance, a "release certificate" will be issued by the supplier. One feature of this type of quality control is that every release certificate must carry the identification number of the contract for which the goods are intended.

Subsequent storage of "released" stocks will also be supervised. Usually it is necessary to set up "bonded stores" where materials for a specific project can be kept apart from all other goods. This procedure prevents any possibility of normal commercial quality stocks from being mixed in with the controlled items. Incidentally, the additional inspection and documentation required for this specialised material handling inflates the cost of most project purchases and must be allowed for in the contract price. This is an example of the choice between purchasing for project or for general stock being taken out of the contractor's hands; project buying has, in fact, become a rigid condition of contract.

STORAGE

Storage, with few exceptions, forms the last link in the material control chain. Whichever method of purchasing has been used, and whatever the type of goods involved, once they have been accepted by the contractor they become an immediate storage problem. The solution could be a very simple matter of placing the goods on a vacant rack. On the other hand, the problem may be a huge lorry, crammed to overflowing with bulky goods which cannot be unloaded because there is just nowhere to put them. Problems of this type differ from pure mental worries. They possess a sickening and grotesque physical reality. If the lorry driver has experienced a long tiring journey, he is hardly likely to be disposed to offer any suggestions – at least none which might prove constructive.

Most problems arising out of the physical storage of goods can be resolved into a few well-defined categories, which are –

1   Space
2   Labelling and identification
3   Location
4   Preservation – shelf life and environment
5   Handling methods
6   Safety
7   Clerical routines
8   Security

Space problems are generally brought about by lack of foresight and by inadequate planning. This is one failing which the project manager should be well equipped to put right. Space is just as much a project resource as labour and materials. It would be feasible to include the space requirements in the project resource allocation planning, although this is seldom done in practice. A simpler, and effective alternative is to provide the materials controller with a copy of the PERT network, or whatever time schedules exist.

Correct labelling of each parcel of items held in stock must be carried out. Otherwise issuing mistakes are bound to arise. Stores staff cannot be expected to identify all the varied items required for a complex project by their appearance. Parts must be given numbers so that ambiguities are impossible. A standard part-numbering discipline, originating from the drawing office, is a necessary basis for a stock-identification system. Each consignment will bear the correct part number on receipt into stores, after goods inwards inspection. Provided that the number and the goods do not become separated, identification is a simple matter. Raw materials can be specified by the appropriate BSS specification and, where appropriate, the cross-section dimensions or thickness.

Location is a problem directly proportional to the size of a stores. Valuable project materials have been known to vanish, so that replacements had to be specially ordered to satisfy immediate project needs. Then, when the project was finished and forgotten, the missing items turned up on a dusty shelf at the back of the stores. The remedy here is to label each shelf, bin, pigeon hole, rack, or hook with an "address code" letter or number. An index of all stock can be used to refer addresses to the appropriate items, listed in part-number order. Any items can then be found easily, provided that the part number is known. This is, of course, a very common procedure in general use in all well-run stores.

Any stocks which are particularly susceptible to deterioration through mechanical shock, heat, or damp must be suitably protected. Some articles will deteriorate under any conditions, and must be used up in a short time. Dry batteries are one example and must be issued in a first in – first out sequence. Certain raw materials are not suitable for storing in close proximity to each other owing to damage through contamination. A housewife would not put a cake of soap next to a packet of tea.

Safe custody and security of stock demands that the storage area can be locked up outside working hours. At other times stores entry will usually be restricted to authorised storekeepers and their assistants. Regulations such as these are not designed only to prevent theft. They also minimise the possibility of irregular withdrawals. "Illegal removals" from stores might arise from surreptitious attempts to disguise shop floor losses or breakages. Overzealous activity to clear shortages on some projects could lead to unauthorised usage of stock preallocated for others.

SHORTAGE LIST

PARTS LIST NUMBER _____ DATE _____ JOB NUMBER _____ ISSUED BY _____ SHEET

ITEM NO	PART NUMBER	DESCRIPTION	QTY ISSUED	QTY SHORT	SUPPLIER	PURCHASE ORDER NO.	DATE PROMISED	DATE RECEIVED

FIGURE 6.5 SHORTAGE LIST FORM
This is a typical shortage list form. Shortage lists are a splendid example of management by exception. They provide at a glance a summary of any materials shortages which are impeding the progress of a project

Clerical routines must be designed and implemented to provide accurate feedback of all material withdrawals to stock control and the cost office. Stock control will rely on this information to update their own records and general stock replacement orders where appropriate. Some organisations require the issue of stores receipt notes for all items received into stores. This could be necessary for internally manufactured assemblies or components which did not pass through goods inwards inspection routines, and therefore did not result in the issue of goods inwards receipt notes. Goods can be issued against individual requisitions, stores issue schedules, or parts lists.

When a parts list, or its equivalent, is passed to the stores as a request for stock issue this is the signal for "kitting" or "kit marshalling" to begin. This activity is the obvious one of pulling all the required items off the shelves, placing them in a box, trolley, or collection area and then amending all associated stores records. Kitting takes time and as such should be included on the PERT network for any project which consumes stored materials.

Kits issued from stores cannot always be complete and occasions will arise when certain items are short. In these cases the storeman will issue a "shortage list" with the kit, and further copies will be distributed among one or two key project people. Recipients might include the shop floor progress chaser, the expeditor, and, of course, the project manager. Shortage lists are a first-class personification of the "management by exception" principle. They focus corrective action on to the real problem areas. A specimen shortage list form is shown in Figure 6.5.

7

MAINTAINING THE PROGRAMME

Once an order or letter of intent has been received, the project ceases to be merely an object for planning consideration and becomes instead a live entity. For the purposes of achieving all the desired project aims, whether technical, budgetary or timescale, every participant must be made fully aware of the particular role which he will be asked to play.

MAKING THE PROJECT COMMITMENTS KNOWN

Normally the technical aspects of a project will fall outside the jurisdiction of the project manager, unless he happens to be doubling the role of project engineer. Budgetary control must fall partly into the area of the company accountant, and the degree of control afforded to the project manager will vary greatly from one firm to another. There can be no doubt, however, regarding the specific duties of the project manager as guardian of the timescale.

We can assume that some degree of planning will be carried out, either in advance, or immediately following receipt of the order. The resulting plans and schedules will do no good at all if they are merely pinned to a wall and regarded thereafter as objects to be gazed at and admired. The first duty of the project manager is to make certain that the contents of these schedules are made known to every departmental manager who is going to become involved in the project.

If a networking session was held, in all probability many of the key project participants will have been present. Therefore, each must have had some share in formulating the plan. This is just as it should be, since no plan can be imposed in isolation. It must carry the blessing and support of all concerned. There are, however, many cases of projects which do not materialise as a firm order until several months have elapsed following the initial planning and tender preparation. During this interval much of the planning detail could have been lost from the memories of the planners. Their memories must be refreshed.

One sound idea is to have the network distributed to every department as soon as the order is received. Either the diagram itself can be reproduced and circulated, or the resource schedule can be used. Possibly a table of activities and their scheduled dates can be issued instead, a more likely procedure if a computer is being used. Naturally, whenever any information is distributed to project members it must be reissued as soon as any changes to the schedules are made. The information must be kept up to date.

ACTIVITY LISTS

Dissemination of programme information can be made far more ffective than the simple blanket distribution of schedules to all and sundry. The project manager can arrange for the schedules to be scanned periodically, either by hand or by computer, and data relevant to separate departments extracted. In this way, lists of activities can be built up, so that every department can be signalled with those activities which are due to start within the immediate future.

In Figure 7.1 a suggested activity list form is shown. The intervals between issues must depend upon the nature of the project and on the number of activities which start and finish each week. In most cases, fortnightly issues will be found sufficient. Only the barest essentials need be listed on the form, in order to keep the information crisp and concise. In the example shown, each department is told the scheduled start and finish dates for every activity which is either in progress or due to start within the next period. Also shown are the estimates, and the cost codes against which all time and materials must be charged. Any other details, such as technical information, or manufacturing instructions, would be shown on drawings or specifications in the usual way.

Activity lists, whilst they could be regarded to some extent as

ACTIVITY LIST	BAUBLE AND GLITTER LIMITED, HALIFAX, YORKSHIRE						PROJECT CODE
TO (DEPT) _____ PERIOD _____ ISSUED BY _____							

ACTIVITY CODE	ACTIVITY NAME	LABOUR GRADE	SCHEDULE		ESTIMATE	
			START	FINISH	MAN-HRS	MATERIALS

FIGURE 7.1 DEPARTMENTAL ACTIVITY LIST
By editing a master project schedule it is possible to advise each department separately of its commitments on a regular basis

being departmental orders, are really nothing more than simple reminders. The exact interpretation must depend upon the documentation arrangements in force within the organisation. Production issues of the lists would be sent to the production control department, who would continue to issue works orders, job tickets, route cards, or any other form of document demanded by the customary procedures understood throughout the company. Activity lists, therefore, need not replace any existing routine paperwork or procedures, but should be regarded as a complementary system.

In many engineering design departments, and other software groups, highly qualified staff will be found whose talents are not being exploited to the full. Whilst technical and scientific aims may be well defined, there always exists a danger that the associated commercial aspects of time and cost are not sufficiently well known. The issue of activity lists can contribute to the more effective use of highly trained specialists in this type of environment by making them aware of their timescale and cost responsibilities. They are provided with general commercial guide lines within which they can concentrate their energies to the company's best advantage.

143

The instructions or reminders contained in activity lists will in no way detract from the personal authority vested in each departmental manager. Although the source of each instruction is the project manager's office, the contents will be injected into the line organisation of the company at suitable points for handing down through the usual channels or supervision. Authority, far from being undermined, will actually be reinforced, since every departmental manager will be provided with more effective tools with which to control the activities of his own particular team.

Instructions are often ignored, simply because they were issued to several individuals collectively, rather than to one specific person. Each member of the group relied upon the others to carry out the instruction, so that in the final event nothing took place at all. A similar danger is created when project networks are distributed to a wide number of departments or people without any explanations or more precise instructions. Activity lists possess the advantage of being absolutely specific to their addressees, so that each recipient knows that every item on his list concerns him directly.

DEPARTMENTAL PROGRESS RETURNS

One prerequisite for any control system is the provision of adequate means for measuring the effect of any commands given. The information so derived can be fed back to the sender in order that errors may be corrected. An artillery commander watches the placing of his shots through field glasses, and uses the visual evidence to correct the aim of his guns. In electrical circuits, signals can be generated which are relative to the position of moving parts or the amplitude of output voltages, in order that the system can be made self-correcting. Project management, as a control system, is no exception. For every instruction which is sent out a resulting feedback signal must be generated, otherwise there will be no means of knowing when corrective actions are required.

If departmental instructions are to be conveyed by means of activity lists, there is no reason why the same basic procedure should not be employed in reverse to carry the feedback responses. When any project is in progress, therefore, it is possible to imagine a two-way system of communication between every departmental manager and the project manager. The only missing item is a document

PROGRESS RETURN	BAUBLE AND GLITTER LIMITED, HALIFAX, YORKSHIRE	PROJECT CODE	
FROM (DEPT) _ _ _ _ _ _ _ _ PERIOD _ _ _ _ _ _ _ _ ISSUED BY _ _			
ACTIVITY CODE	ACTIVITY NAME	PERCENTAGE ACHIEVED	CAN NEXT ACTIVITY START?

FIGURE 7.2 DEPARTMENTAL PROGRESS RETURN
This is the complement of the activity list shown in Figure
7.1. For every command there must be a means for feeding
back the result

complementary to the activity list. This gap can be filled by a
progress return form, a typical specimen of which is shown in
Figure 7.2.

Whatever the design eventually chosen for departmental progress
return forms, care must be taken to avoid ambiguity or any undue
complication. The simpler the form and the easier it can be made to
fill in, the more likely will be the chances of persuading all departmental managers to return them regularly on the due dates. Even
so, training all key participants in the regular routine of progress
reporting often provides project managers with the first real test of
their mettle. Many attempts at project control have broken down
because this particular process was not successfully established.

In the specimen progress return form shown, only information
which is really essential to progress status has been requested. The
sheet is designed to encourage each supervisor to submit his replies
in a style which is best suited to the purposes of the project manager.
The question "can the next activity start?" for instance, demands a
straightforward "yes" or "no" answer, which may be very important
where activities overlap each other in ladder fashion. Sometimes

an engineering job is complete all but the final general assembly drawing, so that procurement lists could be released for most of the long-lead items. The network may not always indicate such possibilities, and very often these opportunities for speeding progress will be missed by individuals unless they are regularly asked the right questions.

The Progress Meeting

In project work, responsibilities often fall between two or more departments, one of which can usually manage to lay blame at the other's door for any shortcomings or apparent negligence. The type of situation which can develop in a factory between engineering and production departments, or between production and inspection interests, is seen all too often. Production delays, for example, are sometimes blamed on to bad design, or on to unwarranted rejections by the inspection department. On some occasions these criticisms will have some foundation. At other times they will not.

When conflicts do arise they must be resolved quickly. Otherwise unprofitable stalemate conditions will be generated, and team harmony will be disrupted. One clear duty of the project manager is to discover the true facts which underlie any interdepartmental problems. He will need to find out these facts not so much to apportion blame as to ensure the continued progress of his project. Often, an impasse is reached, where two departmental managers give separate and different accounts of the reasons for a common problem.

There is only one way in which to overcome these difficulties. The two opposing individuals must be confronted with each other, in the presence of a responsible mediator – logically the project manager. Each individual should now be more reluctant to make excuses which are known to be a variation from the exact truth, because he knows that an instant denial of any unjust criticism will be forthcoming from the other department. More constructively, the person-to-person discussion removes the delays of communication which sometimes exist between impersonalised departments, so that solutions or compromises to common problems can be worked out by mutual co-operation, on the spot. This is one way in which the progress meeting can be born.

Any project manager worthy of the title will want to make certain that whenever possible his tactics are preventative rather than curative. If he finds that a progress meeting can be used to cure problems, then there appears to be no reason why problems could not be prevented altogether by the same means. Progress meetings, with all interested departmental heads present, can be arranged on a regular basis. There is a case for holding meetings frequently, say once a week, on an informal basis at supervisor level, and backing these up with meetings at a more senior level at less frequent intervals. Project review meetings, to discuss the financial prospects in addition to simple progress, can also be arranged, and the general manager would probably want to be present at these.

Regular project progress meetings, therefore, whether chaired by the chief engineer, the production manager, or the project manager, provide a suitable forum where essential two-way communication can take place between planners and participants. The main purposes of the progress meetings emerge as a means of keeping a periodical check on the project progress, and the making of any consequential decisions to implement corrective action if programme slippages occur or appear likely.

The frequency with which meetings are held must depend to a large extent upon the nature of the project and the overall timescale. If they are held more often than is absolutely necessary, there will be some danger of creating general apathy. Departmental managers are usually busy individuals whose time should not be wasted. For the same reason, meetings must be kept short, preferably not exceeding two hours on any one occasion. It may be possible to arrange meetings to start in mid-afternoon, so that there will be some incentive for members to get through all the business before the end of the working day. Discussions should be kept to key topics and irrelevancies swept aside.

There are certain dangers associated with the mismanagement of progress meetings. For instance, it often happens that lengthy discussions arise which are really concerned with technical design problems. These will lead to loss of concentration and interest in the proceedings by those members not involved in the design of the project. Although it is never possible to divorce design considerations from progress topics, design meetings and progress meetings are basically different functions which should be kept apart.

Arguments may break out between individuals during the course of meetings. These may not be altogether undesirable, as meetings must be kept alive, with enthusiasm generated and maintained, provided always that the heat generated can be contained within extinguishable limits. However, an argument must always be resolved within the meeting, so that agreement is reached before the members disperse. If this is not done some continuing friction may result, which is an entirely different condition from healthy enthusiasm and team co-operation.

When a meeting breaks up, it will have been successful only if all the members, on leaving, feel that they have achieved some real purpose and that actions have been decided which will have some practical effect on project progress. Demands made of members during the meeting must be achievable. There will be no point at all in attempting to impose actions to retrieve programme slippages which have already taken the project far beyond the critical limits.

Publication of the minutes must be undertaken without undue delay in order that they do not become outdated by further events before distribution. Minutes should be clearly and concisely written, combining brevity with careful layout so that each action demanded can be seen to stand out from the page. If the document is too bulky, it may not even be read by some recipients. Short pointed statements of fact are all that is required. Every person actioned in the minutes must receive a copy – a point often overlooked. No ambiguities must be allowed after any statement as to the person responsible or the timescale involved. Expressions such as "at the end of next week" or "towards the end of the month" should be discarded in favour of giving actual dates.

PRODUCTION PRIORITIES: IMMEDIATE ACTION ORDERS

Occasions arise when work cannot be loaded to production shops in a logical sequence. If the production control department were able to pick up all orders and load them sequentially, or according to their own machine and manpower schedules, no problems need arise. Sooner or later, however, one order is going to be placed which is wanted urgently and production control will be asked to displace other orders in favour of the newcomer.

Some organisations attempt to allocate order priorities, labelling works orders with letters *A*, *B*, or *C* for example, indicating the degree of urgency with which each particular job is required. It is not difficult to imagine why such systems seldom operate effectively. Naturally, everyone labels his order *A* priority, so that none in fact receives special attention. In the words of W S Gilbert: "When everyone is somebody, then no one's anybody."

A preferable arrangement is for every person who wishes to place an order on a production department to specify some date by which he wants delivery of the completed job or assembly. This at least removes most of the guesswork. The production control department can then signal back whether or not they expect to be able to meet the requested date, or provide an alternative (later) time if that is the best which can be done with the available resources. If the date cannot be met in any particular case, the possibility of subcontracting the work can always be considered.

Special project work often has to take its place in the production organisation alongside routine work or other projects. Conflicts can arise between jobs with urgent priorities, and it is indeed a brave man who attempts to intervene and mediate between two project managers who are fighting for the same production resources. Of course, multi-project resource scheduling, either manually, or by computer, is the logical answer to remove most of the possibility for such conflicts. No matter how good the resource schedules are, however, occasions will crop up when really urgent action must be taken on one particular job, to the exclusion of all others.

The type of job which should demand special attention is that which has come about by unforeseen circumstances on a project which is either very late already, or which carries a severe penalty clause. Prestige contracts may also be found where every production minute counts. Who is to decide whether or not any project really does warrant this kind of special attention? Any disruption to the normal work flow, caused by injecting a job out of turn, is likely to increase general production costs.

One solution to this problem of deciding genuine priorities relies upon the use of special "immediate action orders." These are printed on some highly distinctive card or paper, either brightly coloured or covered with diagonal stripes. Two essential features are necessary to ensure that a proper degree of urgency and respect is always afforded by these immediate action orders. They must be distinguishable by their colour, or by their general presentation so that they stand out like beacons from the routine production orders. Each must be authorised at a very senior level, in order that the order carries sufficient weight, and to prevent the introduction of immediate action orders which are not really justified in the light of the extra costs and disruption which each must create.

Case History. An actual example will now be quoted to illustrate the method by which an immediate action order can be initiated and handled. A project for a complex defence system was well under way. One of the components was a miniaturised high voltage transformer, for use in a compact radar set. The initial production quantities were very small, and at the time in question were limited to the manufacture of a single preproduction prototype.

Each transformer was extremely specialised and great care had to be taken during every manufacturing process to ensure reliability. The coil was sectionally wound on a former which in turn was mounted on an aluminium mandrel. Very high voltages were generated during the operation of the transformer, so that it was necessary to encapsulate the entire assembly, including the mandrel, in epoxy resin. This meant that no component would be reclaimable in the event of failure.

The preproduction transformer took six weeks to produce. Rigorous inspection routines had to be enforced at each assembly sub-stage because the contract was subject to special conditions imposed by HM Government. When the transformer reached the final test stage it was subjected to an overload check, whereupon it developed a short circuit and burned itself out.

The absence of this transformer was recognised as being a very serious set-back to the whole development and production programme. The idea of having to wait a further six weeks for another transformer, as yet unproved in design, was quite untenable. The project manager accordingly raised an immediate action order and asked the general manager to sign it. Authorisation was given, but only after a very careful explanation had convinced the general manager that the action was really justified.

The first result of raising the immediate action order was to preclude the possibility of any further immediate action orders from being issued. The company's rules did not allow any two immediate action orders to be extant at the same time. A progress chaser was allocated full-time to the order, and his first job was to visit the engineering department to obtain design clearance for a replacement transformer. The failure of the first suggested that some modification might be necessary. It was decided that the design of the mandrel was at fault, allowing air bubbles to form during the encapsulation process. These bubbles provided a possible cause for electrical breakdown. The immediate action order, since it was signed by the general manager, carried authority over all departments; this included the engineers and draughtsmen. The fact that a progress chaser was clocking the order into their departments and out again, using a time stamp, was a spur to action, so that modified drawings were made available within about one hour of the order being issued.

By removing another job from a milling machine, and substituting the priority order in its place, the mandrel was manufactured within a very short space of time. Inspection had been alerted to the urgency and they passed the work without any delay, although they did ensure that generally accepted inspection standards were maintained. The progress chaser continued to record the start and finish times of each stage of manufacture. Thus the work was processed through the coilwinding department, the encapsulation department, and finally back to the test laboratory, where the design and construction were now found to be satisfactory.

If any materials shortage had arisen during this urgent programme, the purchasing department would have been expected to get the goods without any regard to cost. If necessary a van would have been sent to collect the missing items from any supplier who could be found with stocks. If a shortage of suitable man-power had caused any difficulty, subcontract labour would have been brought in immediately. Nothing, in fact, would have been allowed to impede the progress of the job.

Without the impetus given by the immediate action order, this job would have required the full production cycle time of six weeks which was taken up by the first transformer. On this special occasion the work was accomplished in only three days. Of course the cost was high. But the programme was saved. In total terms, the cost increase of crashing all the transformer activities was far outweighed by the cost saving in preventing a programme slippage of the whole project.

The reason why such success was achieved with the above example should be appreciated. In the first place, the order was sufficiently rare to command attention from all concerned. It was not "just another high priority order." This condition was safeguarded by the company rule which restricted the total number of immediate action orders issued, so that only one could be in circulation at any point in time. Secondly, the high level of authorisation carried on the documents, together with the implied urgency created by time-stamping every operation, left no doubt in any mind regarding the genuine nature of the crash action request.

If priorities are to be authorised, they must be restricted in number. But, once any job has been given priority status, then all the force and weight of management must be used to back up that decision and ensure that the job is carried right through without interruption. There must be no half measures.

Haste versus Accuracy

A high incidence of modifications arising from design errors could be a direct result of undue haste or crash action introduced when a project was running late. In normal circumstances it would be usual for all drawings to be checked, and for other design calculations to be proved experimentally in a prototype or laboratory model. Possibly occasions will be met when these desirable precautions cannot be put into practice owing to the pressing urgency of the timescale.

One result of pressure on the design function may be to create a temporary shortage of draughtsmen, so that extra men must be made available on a subcontract basis. Men working under these conditions cannot be expected to identify themselves with the project to quite the same extent as full-time employees. Their motivational outlook must be different, and their performance may be at a higher risk because they are unaccustomed to the standards and practice of the firm into which they have suddenly been thrust. If subcontract-produced drawings have to forego the checking procedure, serious doubt may indeed be cast upon the accuracy of the production drawings issued.

When an engineering department or manager is faced with the need to make a conscious choice between speed and accuracy, the ultimate decision must be based upon a reasoned consideration of the consequences which would be met if an error did arise. Suppose, for example, that a small electronic control package had to be produced in a great hurry for an urgent project. If a simple calculation error were made during the design process, then it might be quite easy to rectify the problem during commissioning of the final project, either by changing over a pair of wires, or by substituting some relatively inexpensive components. The risk might be justified in the light of the urgency demanded.

On the other hand, the electronic box might have to contain a circuit laid out on a printed wiring board. Here the problem is slightly different, because rectification of a wiring error might have to await the redrawing and remaking of the board. A more clear-cut case where accuracy cannot be subordinated to speed is that where a high level of production investment is at stake, both in terms of machining hours and raw material costs. If a huge casting has been obtained at considerable expense and has to be machined accurately over a period which consumes many man- and machine-hours, a fundamental design error would be disastrous.

PROGRESS REPORTS

Progress reports addressed to management will have to set out the technical, manufacturing, and financial status of the project and compare the performance in each of these respects to the scheduled requirements. These reports will be issued at regular intervals, and may well be presented by the project manager during the course of project review meetings. Discussion of the facts presented might lead to decisions ranging beyond simple questions of progress. Changes in contract policy or reorganisation may result. It is important, therefore, that data relevant to the condition of the project are presented factually, with any predictions which can be made. The information, because of its detailed nature, will almost certainly not be suitable for distribution outside the company, but must be regarded as proprietary material.

There is another type of management report in addition to the detailed progress reports just described. These are the reports of "exceptions," and are confined in scope to those project factors which are giving rise to acute concern, and which must receive immediate attention if the project is to be held on course. Exception reports can range from selective computer print-outs to the frenzied beating on a senior manager's door by a distraught departmental manager. Before he allows any exception report to be passed on to senior management, the project manager must always assure himself that some simple remedy within his own control cannot be found. Once he has established that events are beyond his control, however, the project manager has a very clear duty to appraise senior management of the facts without delay. This, of course, is following the sensible practice of "management by exception," which helps to ensure that executive effort is employed to the best advantage.

The submission of formal progress reports to the customer could be one of the essential conditions of contract. If any customer does demand the provision of regular written statements of progress, then quite obviously these can be compiled from the same source as those which supplied all the data for internal management reports. Some of the more detailed technical information may not be relevant to the customer's needs, and other details, especially regarding the financial status, should not be the concern of the customer at all. Customer progress reports, therefore, are to some extent edited versions of internal management reports.

If customer reports are to be edited in order to improve clarity and to remove all proprietary information, they must never be allowed to mislead. It is always important to keep the customer informed of the true progress position, especially when slippages have occurred which cannot possibly be contained within the available float. Any attempt to put off the evil day by placating the customer with optimistic forecasts or unfounded promises must lead to unwelcome repercussions later. No one likes to discover that he has been taken for a ride, and customers are no exception to this rule.

8

MODIFICATIONS, BUILD SCHEDULES, AND CONCESSIONS

For many reasons, one could not realistically expect that any special project would pass right through from initial order to final completion without the introduction of at least one change during its active life. The exception to this rule might just possibly exist as a project manager's dream of Utopia, but is not likely to take on any more tangible form.

Origins of Modifications

Whenever changes do arise, they can usually be recognised as belonging to one of two principal categories. They have either been originated within the contractor's own organisation, or they result from a request by the customer. There are also borderline categories which cannot be put into one of these classifications but which contain elements of both. The important distinguishing feature, however, is that linking costs and payment. Will the customer pay for any extra costs, or must the modification be paid for out of project profits? The answer to this all-important question will determine to a very large extent just how any particular change is to be authorised and handled.

Changes requested by the customer could affect the technical specification, in which case they automatically imply a corresponding change to the contract, since the technical specification forms part of the contract documentation. If, as usually happens, the modification results in an increase in the contractor's costs, a suitable change to the contract price must be negotiated. The delivery schedule might also be affected and any resulting delays must be discussed and mutually agreed. Customer-inspired modifications may possess nuisance value and they can disrupt the smooth flow of logically planned work, but they do, nevertheless, offer the prospect of some compensation from an increase in price and possibly even an increase in profits.

If, on the other hand, a contractor finds it necessary to introduce changes himself, he cannot expect to ask the customer to foot the bill. He must be prepared to carry the increased costs himself and answer to the customer for any resulting time delays. Costs arising from a contractor's own modifications must always be very carefully controlled and restricted because they represent a direct charge against project profits.

Estimating the True Costs of a Modification

Most modifications will add to the cost of a project. It is not always appreciated, however, that the total costs of a change can far exceed the straightforward estimate of costs directly attributable to the modification itself. A simple example will help to demonstrate some of the extra incidental costs which can be introduced when a change is made to a project.

Suppose that a project is in hand to produce a single racing car within a small part of a factory engaged on general car production, and, just before completion of the car construction, a general change in the international rules demands that the engine be replaced by one of a slightly different cubic capacity. If the workshop foreman were asked to estimate the cost of changing the engine his answer might turn out something like the following –

Cost of removing old engine	
10 hours at £0.50 an hour	£5.00
Cost of fitting new engine	
15 hours at £0.50 an hour	£7.50
Inspection labour	
3 hours at £0.75 an hour	£2.25
Total direct labour	£14.75
Labour overheads at 150 per cent	£22.12½
Materials, including new engine (bought out)	£195.00
Total cost of modification	£231.87½

This estimate would probably be accepted as fair and reasonable by all concerned. If the work were being carried out for some other firm, on a subcontract basis, then the modification would have to be charged out to them as additional costs, when a mark-up would be added to yield profit. Calculation of the selling price addition should present no difficulty, and could result in a calculation along the following lines –

Estimated factory cost	£231.87½
Add mark-up at 40 per cent	£92.75
Selling price for modification	£324.62½

In the real situation, however, it might take six weeks to obtain the new engine, during which time the project might have to be shelved temporarily. Even assuming that the mechanics could be gainfully employed for this period on other work, it cannot be said that the costs of the modification would be limited to the £231.87½ estimated. The car, together with work benches, jigs, cradles, and special tools would probably occupy some 40m² (about 430 square feet) of work space. The provision of space costs money in rates, heating, lighting, maintenance, and so on.

Under normal conditions these space costs would appear in job cost estimates within the general heading "labour overheads." In practice, the factory accountants find it convenient to work out an annual average ratio between the total direct labour costs and all the combined indirect costs. Direct labour costs include all wages paid to workers actually engaged in productive operations. Indirect costs embrace administrative salaries, the cost of sickness and holiday pay, certain other manufacturing expenses which cannot easily be attributed to any one specific product, and all the costs of providing workspace. By calculating this average ratio it is possible to estimate for all indirect costs thereafter simply by adding a proportional amount to all estimates for direct labour.

If, for example, a factory employs a direct labour force which receives £100 000 a year in wages, and the total indirect costs amount to £150 000, the ratio of direct to indirect costs is 1 : 1·5. The accountants would then set the general overhead rate at 150 per cent. For every hour of direct labour estimated in any job, costs equivalent to another 1·5 hours, or 150 per cent, must be added as labour overheads in order to allow for the associated indirect costs. Provided that enough work is in hand to keep the direct labour force fully employed, all the indirect costs will be recovered automatically in this way.

This system is widely used and works very well until the unexpected comes along to destroy the usually accepted ratio. Sometimes work will be encountered, for instance, which comprises a small amount of direct labour coupled with a substantial amount of bought-out services or materials. The total indirect costs could be higher than the budget yielded by adding 150 per cent to the direct labour content of the job. In the case of the car project, the delay of six weeks was unforeseen and there is no equivalent amount of direct labour being used to support the cost of space over this period.

If the cost office were asked to report on the actual additional costs brought about by the modification in the car case, their findings would probably support the original estimates made by the shop foreman. The cost office would employ standard cost techniques, where they would always assume that the overhead rate of 150 per cent held good. The job costs might therefore show up as profitable. However, when the profit and loss account was prepared for the whole factory, a loss item would appear in respect of the space charges not covered by overheads and this would be labelled as "under-recovery" by the accountants. This is the amount of expenses not recovered as a result of applying the general overhead rate to direct labour estimates. It is a hidden loss, not always appreciated by non-financial project participants.

The actual extent of the under-recovery resulting from the six week stoppage in the car project can be worked out straightforwardly. Assuming that space in this factory costs an all-in total of £10 a year for each square metre, the cost of maintaining 40m² for six weeks would be just over £46. This is half the budgeted profit for the modification, and it has been swallowed up in an invisible loss. On large projects, where the usage of space is greater, disruptions to planned work flow can very soon transform a potential profit into an actual loss. Delays of more than a few days can also be significant in terms of loss of earnings on the capital invested in a project. These factors help to support the oft-quoted phrase "time is money."

If the racing car were delivered too late for the first few meetings of the season, there might be a considerable potential loss in prize money. Other projects could be subject to penalty clauses, or there might be an exhibition opening on a certain date which has to be met. Any delay in the early part of the programme may be reflected in increased activity later on, and this increase in activity could involve crash actions and the intensification of overtime working. All of these considerations represent a threat to profitability.

Modifications often affect stocks of materials by making them redundant. If the racing car team had ordered a spare engine, this, too, might have to be replaced. It is by no means uncommon for quite high value items to be overlooked completely, simply because they are out of sight in some remote storage area.

It is not reasonable to expect that all individuals will inevitably include all possible costs in their estimates, although this would obviously be the ideal target at which to aim. In fact, the project manager must learn to expect that omissions of important cost factors will occur in many estimates. He will become experienced in checking the validity of cost estimates by asking significant and probing questions as a matter of routine, in order that the train of thought of each estimator can be reset. Is there to be no inspection on this job? Are stocks affected? Does the prototype have to be modified too? These are the type of questions which must always be asked if the truth is to be found.

Recording the Actual Cost of a Modification

Some of the difficulties to be expected in assessing the costs of any modification have now been discussed, and it is apparent that there are many factors which could easily be overlooked. Nevertheless, an estimate can be made in most cases, and these estimates can be used to work out any possible increase in the price which the contractor feels able to justify. Recording the actual costs of a modification can prove to be a very much more difficult undertaking, and in fact may be impossible.

The difficulties underlying recording of actual modification costs may not always be appreciated by management, who quite reasonably would like to know just how much their budgets are being affected by changes. Suppose that a man is asked to modify a piece of equipment which has already been completed, inspected, and tested. Here there need be no problem at all in recording costs, because a fresh works order could be issued to authorise the modification alone, and all stripping, reassembly, inspection, and testing could be booked to some specially allocated cost code. If, however, the change were to be introduced into the drawings before completion of the work, an entirely different situation would be created.

Imagine that the equipment to be modified consists of a very complex item of electronic equipment, containing a total of over 10 kilometres of wire, with thousands of connections to be made. Quite often, a change will add new wires, delete some of the existing wires, and add new components. The inspection, not yet started, together with final commissioning will be affected both in scope and complexity. How can anyone be expected to record that part of the work which is directly attributable to any one particular change in these circumstances? It is also probable that many changes will occur on a job of this size before it is finished, so that the only apparent and measurable effect on costs will be to inflate the initial production costs. This situation has to be accepted and if the modification costs are demanded, only estimates can be made.

AUTHORISATION OF MODIFICATIONS

The effects of any modification, whether customer requested or not, may be felt far beyond the confines of the actual area of project directly affected. This could be true of the technical, timescale, or cost aspects. If a project is to be regarded as a technical and commercial system, a change in one part of that system can have consequences elsewhere in the work which the originator might not have been able to foresee. For these reasons alone it is prudent to ensure that every proposed change receives the attention of at least one key member of each project department, in order that the full effects can be predicted as reliably as possible. Naturally, these considerations should normally take place before the modification is put into practice.

In many companies engaged on project work, a regular panel of experts is appointed to deal with the consideration of modifications in order to determine how they must be handled, judging each case separately on its merits. Often, the panel meet regularly on a formal basis and deal with modifications in a batch. Other firms circulate the modifications around the group so that each member considers the effect of the proposed change on his own department. Each method has its advantages and disadvantages. Formal committee sessions, meeting at only monthly intervals for example, mean that delays can be built into the change procedure which might seriously affect the programme. On the other hand, more frequent meetings might take up too much time from the committee members. Informal committees, not meeting collectively but relying on the circulation of documents, suffer from a communication problem and could lead to delays through misunderstanding. Neither approach can be classified as right or wrong, but it will be assumed here that a formal modification procedure, with regular modification committee meetings, exists.

When each change request is considered for approval, the modification committee must weigh up all the possible consequences before giving their recommendations. The specific points which have to be examined can be summarised under the following headings –

1   Apportionment of liability between contractor and customer
2   Cost estimates
3   The additional price (if appropriate)
4   Effect on delivery and timescale generally
5   Effect on reliability and safety
6   Is the change really necessary?
7   The updating of all relevant documentation, including drawings, specifications and instruction manuals
8   If more than one set of equipment is being produced, to decide which of them are to be affected by the proposed change
9   To vet the feasibility of the modification as described by the originator

It is customary to ask any individual who wishes to introduce a change to put his request in writing to the committee. In order to save the committee's time and to ensure that all requests are properly controlled and progressed, it is essential to derive some sort of standard request form. This form must be designed in such a way that the originator will be induced to answer in advance many of the questions which the change committee will want to ask. Even the customer might be encouraged to submit his requests for alterations on the same change request forms. One example of a

HONEYCOMB PRODUCTS LIMITED, LUTON, BEDFORDSHIRE Engineering change request	Mod number Sheet 1 of sheets

PROJECT _____

DRAWINGS AFFECTED

NUMBER	Issue	NUMBER	Issue	NUMBER	Issue	NUMBER	Issue

UNITS TO BE SUBJECTED TO EMERGENCY CHANGE ACTION (IF ANY)

Part number	Serial numbers

CHANGE DETAILS

REASON (IF CUSTOMER REQUESTS ENTER CUSTOMER REFERENCE _____)

ORIGINATOR _____   Date _____   Estimated cost £ _____

COMMITTEE DECISION: LIST POINT OF EMBODIMENT, ACTION ON STOCK, LIMITATIONS

Approved/rejected _____

FIGURE 8.1   ENGINEERING CHANGE REQUEST FORM
A document which allows effective consideration and
recording of modifications

standard form is illustrated in Figure 8.1, but this is only one of a wide variation of possible versions, the titles of which can include "engineering change order," "modification request," and many others.

In practice, these requests will have to be registered by some clerical individual before they are seen by the committee. This clerk may reside in the contracts office, the project manager's office, the engineering department, or in some other department. He will allocate a serial number to every request, which provides each potential modification with its own identity. The register will be used as a progress check, to ensure that all requests are seen by the committee within a reasonably short time. For changes which are approved, the register provides a means for following them up, to make absolutely certain that new issues of drawings do, in fact, result.

Anyone who is employed within the contractor's organisation, regardless of seniority, could be allowed to put forward a change request without any real risk to the project. Each request has no authority until it has received the committee's approval. There is no danger, therefore, that unwelcome changes will be introduced into the actual project work by all and sundry, whilst the possibility of changes beneficial to a contract as a result of suggestions from junior members will not be entirely ruled out.

Modifications can usually be described as being either "essential" or "desirable." When the committee is faced with a request for a modification which is seen to be essential, they have very little choice in deciding whether or not to give their approval. The only real question in such cases would hinge upon a determination of the feasibility of the proposed method.

"Desirable" modifications are a different kettle of fish altogether, and the modification committee will normally reject all of them if they are doing their job conscientiously. The only exceptions will be those proposals which can be shown to have undeniable advantages in terms of costs, or which would bestow some other benefit on the project to the advantage of the contractor. Unfortunately, many promises of the good things to come from the introduction of changes turn out to be far less beneficial than the original estimates might have suggested. Before any so-called desirable change is approved, all possible consequences must be very carefully examined and the cost estimates checked. It is no good introducing a change which saves a few pounds on a particular assembly if by so doing the whole programme is delayed by a few weeks whilst new parts are awaited and the idle time results in costs amounting to several hundreds of pounds.

EMERGENCY MODIFICATIONS

We live in an impatient age, and project time can usually be regarded as a scarce commodity. If the need for an essential modification is discovered during the active production phase of a programme, there may simply be no time available in which to reissue suitably changed drawings. There are right and wrong ways of dealing with this situation and the following case history is a good, all too common example of the latter.

Case History. Kosy-Kwik Limited were a company which specialised in the supply and installation of heating and ventilating equipment. In 1960 they were awarded a contract, as subcontractors to a large building group, to plan and install all the central heating arrangements in a new multi-storey office block commissioned by the Coverite Insurance Company Limited. Two engineers, Clarke and Jackson, were assigned to the project. Whilst Clarke was given overall design responsibility, Jackson was detailed off to plan the central control panel and its associated controls and instrumentation.

We join the project during the height of the prefabrication period in the Kosy-Kwik factory. By this time, all deliveries of plant and equipment to the Coverite premises had been made or arranged and the major part of the remaining factory work comprised the completion of the control panel.

Jackson was a conscientious engineer and took a great interest in his work as it progressed through the factory. He was in the habit of making periodical tours, in order to keep a check on progress and on the results of his designs. It was during one of his routine tours that Jackson was approached one day by the foreman of the sheet metal shop. It appeared that the control panel, now welded together, displayed a somewhat weak front panel.

Jackson could only agree with the foreman's opinion. The front panel was indeed decidedly flimsy, as a result of an obvious design error in specifying a gauge of steel which was far too thin. Delivery of the control panel to site was critical to the success or otherwise of meeting the contract completion date. There was no time available in which to strip the panel down and replace the whole front panel. In any case, the cost of such an operation at this stage would have been prohibitive. A simpler solution had to be found.

The engineer asked the foreman to weld some chunky pieces of channel iron on to the rear face of the panel in order to stiffen it up. The foreman agreed that this would be a possible solution, but refused to carry out the request without a drawing. Otherwise, as he explained, he would stand no chance of getting the job passed by inspection. Jackson resolved this dilemma by taking out his pen, marking up the pieces of channel iron on the foreman's copy of the panel drawing, and then signing the alteration.

The modification was successful. Everyone concerned was very relieved, not least Jackson, whose reputation had been likely to suffer. Only a few hours were lost, and the panel was, in fact delivered on the correct date. The remainder of the project went ahead without any further mishap and Coverite Limited was added to a long list of previously satisfied customers.

Some two years passed by, during which time several changes occurred in the organisation of Kosy-Kwik Limited. Clarke received a well-deserved promotion to a branch office, where he became area manager. Jackson retired to enjoy his pension. The engineering department expanded and attracted many new recruits. Among these was an experienced contract engineer named Stevens. He had never met either Clarke or Jackson and now had no means of contact with either of them.

In the summer of 1963, Kosy-Kwik were awarded a follow-up contract by the Coverite Insurance Company. The offices were to be extended with a new wing to house computer services and staff. Coverite were working to a tight and well-planned time schedule which demanded the opening of the new wing on the first day of 1964. Because of the rigid timescale restrictions, several contract conditions were imposed on Kosy-Kwik. In particular, the only shutdown period allowed for the existing central heating plant, in order to connect up the additional circuits, was to be during the Christmas holiday, to avoid any loss of work by the office staff. There was also to be a penalty payment of £100 for every week or part of a week by which Kosy-Kwik failed to meet the scheduled end-date.

Stevens was appointed as engineer in charge. He decided that the best policy would be to construct as many parts of the project as possible in the factory, on a prefabrication basis. By following this procedure, the amount of work to be done during the short time available on site would be reduced to an absolute minimum, and there would be a greater chance of completing the installation during the Christmas break. He found a roll of drawings labelled "Coverite Project" in a dead-file drawer, dusted them off, and set to work.

Most of the system was found to be straightforward, and the final tying-in with the existing installation was to be achieved by the provision of a bolt-on control package which could be fitted to the original control panel. This package was duly designed, manufactured, and delivered to site along with all the other essential materials. By the time Christmas arrived, all pipes and radiators had been placed in position in the new building and connected up. All that remained was for the final installation team to arrive, shut down the plant, connect the new system into the boiler, modify the control panel with the kit provided, and then test the whole system.

On Christmas Eve two fitters were sent to shut down the plant and start work on the control panel. After unloading all their tools, the first job was to cut a rectangular hole in the existing control panel in order to fit the new control package. A template had been provided for this purpose which they now placed in position. It was at this time that the men discovered several large ribs of heavy channel iron welded on to the rear face of the panel. These ribs made the work of hole cutting far more difficult than had been expected, since the two men had only come prepared to tackle the thin sheet indicated on the old drawings. Several hours, and hacksaw blades later, the hole was finished. Then it was found that all the rear connections to the new control package were fouled by what remained of the channel iron. Worse still, the front panel was now decidedly weak and flimsy.

The two men were experienced and trained as skilled installation fitters, but were not equipped materially or mentally to deal with problems of this magnitude unaided. They suffered an acute sense of frustration and isolation, although they found different words with which to express their feelings. A cry for help was indicated, but unfortunately the response to their telephone call to Kosy-Kwik headquarters was less than satisfactory. To the background accompaniment of a rather spirited office party, they learned that all the engineers had departed for the Christmas holiday. There was no choice left to the two fitters other than to follow the engineers' example, and go home.

There is no real need to dwell at length on the consequence of this case, which can best be summed up by a short summary of the additional cost items. These were –

1	Design and manufacture of one new control package and modification kit	£150
2	Costs and expenses incurred during first visit of installation fitters	£20
3	Costs for repairing weakened front panel, on site	£10
4	Penalty clause, operative for four weeks at £100 a week	£400
	Total additional costs, directly attributable	£580

A retrospective glance over the circumstances which led up to the disastrous consequences of the "Coverite" project will provide a useful basis for describing a more reliable method of dealing with very urgent modifications. Notice that in the example just given all the troubles can be traced back to the introduction of a marked-up print on the shop floor, the details of which were not transposed on to the contract file drawings. Unfortunately, although the use of marked-up prints is generally to be deplored, we have to be realistic about this problem and accept that occasions will be encountered when there is simply no time in which to up-date and reissue new prints from the master drawings. Under these circumstances some sort of temporary documentation must suffice.

Safeguards. One way in which the up-dating of final drawings can be safeguarded in the event of emergency changes relies on the streamlining of the existing modification procedure, but does not by-pass any of the actual control points. The originator of the modification writes out an engineering change order, and then gets it registered by the clerk. After seeking the immediate approval of the chief engineer or his deputy, he passes one copy of the engineering change order to the drawing office for their eventual action on the master drawings. Another copy is kept by the registration clerk, who makes sure that it is seen at the next session of the modification committee. The original version of the engineering change order is passed to production control, or the departmental supervisor involved, and this becomes part of the issued manufacturing instructions.

Once an emergency change instruction has been issued to a production area, the actual engineering change order must accompany the working drawings and other manufacturing instructions right through all subsequent stages, especially including inspection. In the event of the working prints having to be marked up, which may be inevitable owing to insufficient space on the change order form, an identical marked-up print must be sent to the drawing office at the same time, in order that they are provided with the facts to record in the official drawing system. Modern photographic techniques take only a few minutes, and, apart from saving time, this ensures that errors in copying will not be introduced.

BUILD SCHEDULES

In the case of the Coverite project, the original installation was only concerned with the supply of one complete set of equipment, all the details of which could be recorded at the time on one set of drawings and specifications. Some projects involve the repetitive manufacture of parts or assemblies which have to be supplied according to a delivery schedule which extends over a considerable period of time. When this happens, there is a danger that changes will be introduced at the factory during the course of the project, so that some units which have already been finished or delivered will not be affected, whilst others, which are in current production or not yet started, will be subjected to the change.

The modification committee may, in fact, decide to withdraw some or all of the units which have already been supplied to the customer, in order that they may be modified to bring them up to the latest design standard. On the other hand, the committee could arrange for modifications to be introduced selectively, so that only some units would be affected. If a project is considered which does result in a number of identical units scattered about the production floor, the customer's premises, and possibly even other locations, it is obviously important for a number of reasons that the contractor knows the exact standard to which each has been manufactured.

The first requirement is that each unit should be identifiable by some mark which distinguishes it from its fellows. This objective is usually achieved by the allocation of serial numbers. These, together with a type number or part number enable any unit to be identified positively, with no possible fear of misinterpretation. A voltmeter type 10256, serial number 1023, leaves no room for doubt. When this unit is received back at the factory for servicing or repair, it can be recognised as one particular voltmeter, and there is no question regarding its origin.

If a modification is made which changes an item to the extent that it can no longer be directly interchanged with its unmodified counterpart, the part number must be changed. This is a golden rule, to which no exception should ever be allowed. Normally, however, modifications will simply result in the reissue of drawings with revised issue numbers. Since a reissue will take place every time a modification is incorporated, it follows that the build standard of any unit could be indicated by reference to the issue number and part number of the general assembly drawing to which it was constructed. Unfortunately, although this might seem a feasible statement in theory, it is not always true in fact as the following example will show.

Suppose that a succession of units are to be made which are all basically identical and which have to be delivered singly over a fairly long period. Each unit is really a box containing electrical components, wired together and tested as an assembly. If no modifications have been introduced, the general assembly drawing would probably stand at issue 1. If the number of this drawing is 11223344, then the first unit to be produced could be identified as a box, type 11223344, serial number 001. Provided that production control or inspection had kept adequate manufacturing records, it should be possible to turn up the relevant entries and discover that this unit had been made to issue 1 of the general assembly drawing, which would imply that no modifications were incorporated.

Now imagine the situation if a modification were to be introduced which affected only some of the later boxes. For the sake of argument, the change might affect the specification of one of the electrical components. If this did happen, the general assembly drawing itself might not be affected because the wiring and layout would remain unchanged. Only the parts list would be changed, so that the sheet affected would have to be changed to issue 2. Now all drawings would still be at issue 1, except for one sheet of the parts list. If the modification were introduced at serial number 020 onwards, and a unit were to be returned for repair bearing the serial number 025,

BUILD SCHEDULE											
FOR _____(ASSEMBLY)							Number		Issue		
SERIAL/BATCH NUMBERS											
Approved by _____ Date _____							Sheet of sheets				
DRAWING NUMBER	Sheet no	Issue	DRAWING NUMBER	Sheet no	Issue		DRAWING NUMBER	Sheet no	Issue		
MODIFICATION NUMBERS INCORPORATED (to be completed on sheet I only)											
HONEYCOMB PRODUCTS LIMITED, LUTON, BEDFORDSHIRE											

FIGURE 8.2 A TYPICAL BUILD SCHEDULE SHEET
A build schedule is used to specify the modification state
and hardware content of a project. This is achieved by
listing all drawings and associated documents together
with the correct issue numbers

the production records would still show that it had been built to issue 1 of the general assembly drawing. The modification would not be revealed.

The most common method of circumventing this problem is tedious but possibly unavoidable. A list has to be compiled of all the drawings which are to be used in the manufacture of every unit, and the correct issue numbers of all sheets must be shown. This document will either be compiled separately for every single unit or will sometimes be arranged to cover particular production batches. In all cases the units will be identified specifically by listing their serial or batch numbers. The inspection department then carry out their task with reference to the build schedule, to ensure that the correct drawings issues have been used through manufacture. Note that the correct issues may not always be the *latest* issues.

An example of a build schedule sheet is shown in Figure 8.2. Every time a modification affects the unit covered by a particular version of the build schedule, the schedule, too, must be up-dated and given a new serial number. By this means a foolproof system can be set up from which the actual standard of manufacture of any unit can be determined after it has left the factory. The serial number of each unit enables the inspection department to scan their records and find out the issue of the build schedule which applied to the unit. The drawing office would keep a set of back-issue drawings, so that it would be possible to reassemble a set of all the relevant manufacturing drawings and specifications for the unit in question.

A build schedule (sometimes called a "master record index" among a variety of other names) is seen to be a simple extension of a product drawing list. Indeed, once a drawing list has been prepared, the same set of translucent masters can be used as a basis from which sub-masters can be taken to get the preparation of build schedules under way. By this means, the amount of clerical effort required can be substantially reduced. For many Government contracts, the establishment of build schedules may be mandatory, but the amount of work normally involved in their preparation and upkeep often deters companies from using them for purely commercial contracts.

A practical and safe method exists for indicating the actual modification state of any unit which does not rely on inspection records. This is really an extension of the build schedule system and consists simply of fitting a label to every unit which lists the modifications which have been incorporated. Whereas a build schedule will define the correct standard to which any unit of known serial number *should* be built, the modification label will show the changes *actually* incorporated. Needless to say, as each fresh modification is made to any unit, the modification label must be suitably up-dated by the addition of the appropriate modification serial number.

There are, of course, limitless variations possible for recording and controlling modifications and build standard records. It is not suggested that the methods described above are in any way the best, or ideal for all organisations. Each project creates its own demands, and these must always be met according to the particular administration policies which are in force. The important point to be made is that once modifications have taken place it is essential to provide some method for keeping orderly records of their incorporation. Many firms which start out on project work realise this fact too late, and are faced with the servicing and maintenance of equipment in the field for which they have no valid drawings.

CONCESSIONS

Production departments, faced with the need to keep to a budget or to accomplish work within a scheduled timescale, sometimes find that they need to depart from the specific instructions contained in the manufacturing drawings in order to achieve their objective. Naturally, the inspection department will keep a wary eye open to ensure that no unauthorised shortcuts or botching is allowed.

Suppose, however, that a drawing specifies the use of chromium plated screws, but that these are simply not available when required because they are some awkward thread. The purchasing department may be able to obtain alternative screws with a cadmium plate finish, or possibly some other thread could be substituted. If the production team decided to make this substitution without reference to the design engineers, there would be some danger (remote in many companies) of the inspection department noticing the difference, and rejecting the work because it deviated from the drawing.

But would the use of these alternative screws matter? Well, of course it all depends upon the actual situation and whether the screws are in a prominent position where they will be easily seen if they do not match other chromium parts. Someone has to decide, and either authorise or reject the switch. In any project one indivi-

172

dual can usually be singled out as having supreme design responsibility. He is in fact the design authority and may be personified in the chief engineer, the project engineer, the design draughtsman, or some other suitably qualified man.

If a request for some manufacturing concession does receive the approval of the design authority, this is something less than a full design modification. It is most unlikely that the drawings will ever be up-dated to suit the change, although a record of the variation from drawing will be kept in the inspection records. A concession is, as its name implies, the granting of official permission to depart from the drawing standard. Whenever a concession is granted, the same sort of questions must be asked by the design authority as if a modification were being considered. Safety, reliability, performance, interchangeability must all be taken into account and the possible consequences weighed up before a decision can be reached.

Procedures for requesting concessions vary greatly from one company to another, and may range from the very informal, "Is it OK if we do it this way instead, George?" to a rigid discipline supervised by the inspection department. The latter situation is much more likely to be experienced when Government contracts are being undertaken, in which case not only the contractor's own engineers and inspectors have to be satisfied with the concessions, but also the Government's own inspecting authority, which will take a very keen interest.

Concessions can arise in three basically different ways. Corresponding with these possibilities are three types of form, any one of which could result in the granting of a concession, in appropriate circumstances. The first case is that already illustrated by the example of the chromium plated screws. Here, the production department discovered in advance that they would be unable to fulfil the requirements of the drawings within the available timescale, and were able to propose their own suggested alternative solution. The resulting "request for concession" would normally be submitted on a form similar to that shown in Figure 8.3. Registration and authorisation would be carried out on a similar basis to that for an emergency modification, although the drawings would not, of course, be updated.

One feature which is typical of project production activity is that the drawings are often completely new and untried. It is not surprising, therefore, that a higher incidence of initial production

```
┌─────────────────────────────────────────────────────────┬───────────────┐
│              REQUEST  FOR  CONCESSION                     │ Serial number │
├─────────────────────────────────────────────────────────┴───────────────┤
│ PART NUMBER _____ ISSUE _____ BATCH/SERIAL NUMBERS _____ │
│                                                                           │
│                                     WORKS  ORDER  NUMBER _____ │
│ This requests a deviation from the above drawings for the parts defined by │
│ the above batch/serial numbers only in the following respects             │
│                                                                           │
│                                                                           │
│                                                                           │
│                                                                           │
│                                                                           │
│                                                                           │
│                            Requested by _____ Date _____         │
├───────────────────────────────────────────────────────────────────────────┤
│ Reason for request                                                        │
│                                                                           │
│                                                                           │
├──────────────────────────────────┬────────────────────────────────────────┤
│ This concession  does not affect  │ Approved/rejected *                    │
│    Reliability                    │                                        │
│    Safety                         │ _____        │
│    Interchangeability             │         CHIEF  ENGINEER                │
│                                   │ _____        │
│                                   │         CHIEF  INSPECTOR               │
├──────────────────────────────────┴────────────────────────────────────────┤
│ HONEYCOMB  PRODUCTS  LIMITED,  LUTON,  BEDFORDSHIRE                        │
└───────────────────────────────────────────────────────────────────────────┘
```

* Delete as appropriate

FIGURE 8.3   ONE TYPE OF CONCESSION REQUEST FORM
A means of controlling and authorising departures from
specific drawing instructions

problems is frequently a characteristic of project work. The difficulties which can be encountered range from obvious design errors to simple interpretation problems. Design errors must, of course, be corrected by the introduction of suitably up-issued and corrected drawings, for which the full-scale modification procedure will usually be invoked. Simple problems associated with the interpretation of drawing instructions can be resolved in a matter of minutes by an explanation on the spot from the appropriate engineer. Between these two extremes lies a no-man's-land of production difficulties which are not a direct result of errors, but which demand more than a simple explanation to get production on the move again.

In some firms, these "in-between" problems are channelled into a

ENGINEERING QUERY	Serial number

PART NUMBER _____ ISSUE _____ WORKS ORDER NUMBER _____

Is work held up? YES/NO

QUERY: to engineering department

Department _____ Date _____ Raised by _____ (FOREMAN)

ANSWER

Signed _____ (SENIOR ENGINEER) Date _____

CONCESSION APPROVAL (if appropriate)
The above instructions to deviate from drawings
will not affect reliability/interchangeability/safety   (CHIEF ENGINEER) _____

(CHIEF INSPECTOR) _____

HONEYCOMB PRODUCTS LIMITED, LUTON, BEDFORDSHIRE

FIGURE 8.4 ENGINEERING QUERY NOTE
This form provides a means of controlled communication
between design engineers and manufacturing departments
whenever production difficulties are encountered

175

formalised "engineering query" procedure, which relies on the use of forms of the type shown in Figure 8.4. The general idea is that the production individual who comes up against a problem, writes out his difficulties on one of these forms and submits it to the engineering department for an answer. Naturally, the system can only operate effectively if each request is afforded reasonably urgent consideration. The advantages provided by adopting this routine are that all requests can be registered and progressed by the engineering clerk, similarly to modifications, in order to ensure that none is forgotten altogether, and to keep production personnel physically out of the engineering department.

The sort of problem which could give rise to an engineering query note would be that concerned with the use of adhesives. If the recommended adhesive failed to produce the specified bond strength, so that when the clamps were removed the work disintegrated into its constitutent parts, the production team would probably want to ask the engineers for an alternative course of action. If the problem were to prove too difficult to sort out on the spot, the engineers might be forced to return the query note with a temporary solution suggested. The instruction might read: "Clean off adhesive, and use pop-rivets instead. This instruction applies only to batch 1. Drawings will be reissued with alternative adhesive for batch 2."

As soon as an engineering query note is returned to a production department with instructions which conflict with those given in the manufacturing drawings, the query note becomes an authority to deviate from drawings. As such, the authorised query note has become a concession. The query note would be attached to the manufacturing drawings in these circumstances and this would enable the job to be cleared through inspection. The results which can occur from the use of engineering query notes are so closely allied to the application of concession request forms that it is wasteful not to consider combining the two procedures, and designing one all-purpose form to cope with both needs.

Suppose that a block of extremely expensive raw material has been subjected to a protracted period of machining by highly skilled operators, but on final inspection one of the dimensions is found to be marginally outside limits of tolerance. If the error has resulted in the work being undersized, and no rectification is possible, the inspector has no choice other than to reject the job, and to write

INSPECTION REPORT	Serial number

PART NUMBER _ _ _ _ _ _ _ _ _ _ ISSUE _ _ _ _ _ _ BATCH/SERIAL NUMBERS _ _ _ _ _ _ _ _ _ _

TEST SPEC _ _ _ _ _ _ _ _ _ _ ISSUE _ _ _ _ _ _ WORKS ORDER NUMBER _ _ _ _ _ _ _ _ _ _

The above unit(s)/assembly/part(s) have failed to satisfy the requirements of the relevant drawings and specifications in the following respects

INSPECTOR _ _ _ _ _ _ _ _ _ _ _ _ Date _ _ _ _ _ _ _ _ _

REQUEST FOR CONCESSION (to be completed if appropriate)

The above discrepancies do not affect reliability/safety/interchangeability

Other remarks

Signed _ _ _ _ _ _ _ _ _ _ _ _ _ _
(CHIEF ENGINEER)

DISPOSAL DECISION	SERIAL NUMBERS	AUTHORISATION
SCRAP AND REMAKE		
RECTIFY AND RE–INSPECT		(CHIEF INSPECTOR) _ _ _ _ _ _ _ _ _
CONCESSION GRANTED		_ _ _ _ _ _ _ _ _ _ Date

HONEYCOMB PRODUCTS LIMITED, LUTON, BEDFORDSHIRE

FIGURE 8.5 INSPECTION REPORT FORM
A method for reporting and recording defects or deficiencies
discovered by the inspection department

out a report giving his reasons. The engineers, on seeing the inspection report, might decide that the error is too small to justify the scrapping of such an expensive piece of work. The inspection report could be suitably annotated with an instruction authorising clearance of the work, either fully, or for some restricted purpose. Here is another method by which work can be passed through inspection although it does not strictly conform to manufacturing drawings. The inspection report has been translated into another form of concession. Figure 8.5 shows a suitable form.

The reasons for instituting concession discipline are fairly obvious, since any departure from issued drawing instructions must always be carefully watched. Concession records may have less significance than other project records once the work has been finished and delivered. Nevertheless, they can prove useful in the quality control function, especially in the event of failures or faults which develop in delivered equipment, where they may enable the contractor to trace the causes of failures or of deterioration in performance. If one of a number of identical units fails, it may be vital to trace all other units which contained a particular concession in order that further failures can be prevented.

The procedures associated with the authorisation and granting of concessions can exist in a wide variety of permutations and combinations of the methods described. Whichever method a company decides to adopt, the concession register will be complementary to the manufacturing drawings, modification records, inspection and test records, and build schedules in defining the exact composition of the completed project.

9

RELATING ACHIEVEMENT
TO EXPENDITURE

Many large projects, spread out over a timescale lasting several
months or more, could well involve the investment of large sums of
the contractor's money. By the time the contract is completed and
paid for, the resulting profits might be offset or nullified by the cost
of the capital employed. In other words, the firm has been forced
to pay substantial interest on the money borrowed to finance the
project, or alternatively has had its own money tied up unprofitably.
For these reasons, "progress" or "stage" payments are sometimes
agreed between the contractor and his customer. This enables some
invoices to be raised during the course of the project, so that the
contractor is not called upon to invest the whole cost of the project
before final payment is made.

The basis for making stage payment claims may be cut and dried
contractually, being dependent upon completion of certain stages
in the project, or on the deliveries of specific items of equipment to
the customer. In other cases no such stages will be defined and
progress payments are made at regular intervals, the amounts being
decided according to the actual progress achieved as certified by the
contractor. It is obviously very important that such achievement
can be accurately measured for this purpose, to ensure that invoicing
is kept in step with real progress.

In the event of claims which are too low, because the assessment
of achievement has been understated, the contractor will be missing
his opportunity for reaping the maximum possible profits with
minimum delay. On the other hand, if achievement is overstated, the
higher stage payments which will result can lead to other troubles.
The customer is hardly likely to be pleased when he eventually dis-
covers that after paying up for most of the work, delivery is late. He is

going to feel that he has been deceived. The contractor may also have misled himself into spending profits which he has not in fact made.

If a project is to be financially controlled with any degree of success, three factors must assume major significance in the considerations. These are budgets, the costs incurred, and the progress achieved in relation to those costs. A knowledge of the budgets and costs by themselves will be of no use at all unless the corresponding progress can be gauged. All three basic factors must therefore be monitored during the active project life.

The establishment of budgets should present no real problem, since these can be derived from the departmental estimates and amended from time to time to allow for any project modifications which may be ordered by the customer. Cost recording will be an established routine in any well run firm, so that records of project costs at any time can always be demanded from the cost office. The only possible difficulty which can be expected in cost analysis is the time delay which must inevitably occur between the actual expenditure and the corresponding entry in the books. Achievement analysis is not, however, part of the normal procedure of most companies, and this, therefore, is the missing link in any attempt at financial control.

Imagine a bricklayer, engaged in the building of a wall which is to be 15 metres long and 3 metres high. This man could, in fact, be working on one small facet of a much larger project, so that the bricklaying activity might be represented on the arrow diagram by one arrow labelled "lay bricks – boundary wall," or something to that effect. If at any time during the course of his labours we needed to know just how much had been achieved, a simple count of the number of bricks laid would provide the answer. Alternatively, the area of wall built could be measured. Simple arithmetical processing of the result will yield an answer expressed as a percentage of the whole job. If, for example, the wall is to contain 4000 bricks, when 3000 bricks have been laid, the work is obviously 75 per cent complete.

Now consider a design engineer, also engaged on one project activity, and suppose that his particular job has been scheduled to take ten weeks to completion. How can any sensible measurement of achievement be made on this intangible task? One could perhaps attempt to use the passage of time as a rough guide, so that when three weeks have elapsed the job is considered to be 30 per cent complete. Alternatively, the actual bookings to the job could be obtained and progress assessed from the man-hours expended. Any assumption based on these foundations would indeed be most unwise and dangerous, for many obvious reasons. The engineer may have been interrupted in his work through lack of design information or he may just be a slow worker. It is also more than possible that the original estimate could have been intrinsically wrong. The best that can be done in these circumstances is to ask the engineer, or his superior, for an opinion. "What percentage of this task do you consider has been achieved?" might be asked, or, perhaps more provocatively, "How much longer will this job take?"

In the case of the bricklayer, the answer obtained was objective, accurate, and proof against fear of sensible contradiction. Engineering, draughting, and other software activities are far less straightforward and much more difficult to assess in terms of progress achieved quantitatively. The engineer may have been guilty of a bad error of judgement when he gave his progress report. This is the penalty which must be paid when changing from an objective measurement to a subjective assessment of progress. Nevertheless, there is no need for too much despondency. At least an answer of sorts was extracted from the engineer, and this is far better than no answer at all.

Now suppose that instead of looking at only one individual activity, a progress assessment has to be made for a large project. Many hundreds of different activities may be involved, some of which are not started, whilst others will be in progress and several could be completely finished. Measurement is not now directed at the work of one man, or even one department, but at the whole range of project participation. Design tasks, production, testing, inspection, installation, and commissioning are all possible fields of activity which might have to be taken into account. Now where does the answer lie? There is no one individual who can be approached for an achievement assessment. The chief engineer, production controller, or in fact any other departmental manager, will not be able to comprehend the full scope of achievement by himself. No answer will be forthcoming at all unless special steps are taken to set up a measurement system.

The first stage necessary in the establishment of an effective procedure for the monitoring of achievement is quite simple. A decision has to be made to decide how many different categories of costs are to be considered. There is no real choice open here, since the cost centres used to establish the original project estimates will provide the most logical key. These cost centres will probably correspond either to different departments or to various grades of labour. Departmental achievement analysis can be extremely valuable because it allows each departmental manager to be given real objectives, against which his performance can be measured.

DESIGN ACHIEVEMENT

Most projects start their real life in a design department, and the first illustration of achievement analysis can conveniently be taken from that area. Suppose that an engineering team has been charged with the responsibility for completing the design of a project containing 200 separate design activities. The total departmental budget, derived from an addition of all the estimates, is 1000 man-weeks, but the estimated times for individual activities vary from as little as half a man-week to twenty man-weeks.

Now imagine that the project is spread over an extended time span, and that a point in time has been reached where 500 man-weeks of engineering have been spent. By simple prediction, if half the budget has been spent, one should expect that half the work has been finished, or in other words, achievement should be 50 per cent. No person in his right mind could assume this direct relationship to hold good however, since there is no guarantee whatever that the estimates were right in the first place or that work has proceeded according to plan.

No attempt to assess a complex situation of this kind can really be started without the aid of a logical work breakdown. Each separate job can then be given a "work value," expressed in convenient units and directly proportional to the expected cost in man-time. As each job is finished, the appropriate number of units can be added to a tally of completed work. This running total can then be compared at any time to the original number of work units which comprised the departmental project load. A direct measurement of percentage achievement then becomes a matter of proportional arithmetic.

Fortunately, this process is far less complicated than it sounds.

The basic work breakdown, together with the convenient units of work, already exists in the shape of the project task list and its associated estimates. The total estimate for each department must already be known and every single activity comprising the main task list will boast its own estimate of man-time.

Now it is possible to return to the example of the engineering design department. A good first-shot attempt at measuring achievement can be made by counting up the estimates for all completed activities. Remember that 500 man-weeks have been spent out of a total budget of 1000 man-weeks. Suppose that 80 activities have been finished, the estimates for which add up to 450 man-weeks. It is now apparent that 450 man-weeks of the total work value have been achieved, representing a percentage achievement of 45 per cent.

At first sight an achievement of 450 man-weeks for the expenditure of 500 man-weeks appears to indicate an overspend of 50 man-weeks. However, a significant amount of achievement could well be tied up in work in progress. The result of 45 per cent is therefore likely to be too low, and must be re-examined. The remedy lies in obtaining percentage progress reports for all activities which are in progress at the time of measurement. Corresponding portions of their estimates can then be added to the completed work tally, to yield the true total achievement.

As the work in progress accounts for only a small proportion of the whole project, errors in its assessment will have little overall effect. This will of course be less true for short-term projects, where the proportion of work in progress at any time may be rather high. If the sizes of individual tasks are large, owing to an insufficient work breakdown in the preparation of the task list, then again work in progress may rank high, since it will take correspondingly longer to cross off completed activities. We must assume, however, that the task list was correctly prepared, so it is only in the short-term projects that errors will prove significant. In any case, it is in the long-term projects that achievement measurement becomes of most use in predicting overspends in time to allow corrective action or in evaluating the fair levels at which progress payments can be claimed from the customer.

If, in the example taken, 40 man-weeks of achievement was the assessed amount of completed work in progress, then the total achievement would be amended to 490 man-weeks, which is a percentage completion of 49 per cent. An actual expenditure of 500 man-weeks is now seen to involve an overspend of only 10 man-weeks. Now suppose that the assessment of 40 man-weeks work-in-progress achieved was in error by as much as ±50 per cent. The total significance is only 20 man-weeks in 490, or about ±4 per cent.

In this example, therefore, one can declare with a fair degree of confidence that, at the instant of measurement, 49 per cent of all engineering had been achieved. Naturally care must be taken to ensure that the actual costs of 500 man-weeks were recorded up to the same date as the achievement check. Given the information which has been recorded or derived so far, it is possible to embark upon a process of simple linear extrapolation in order to predict the final departmental expenditure at project completion.

Information received so far–
    500 man-weeks have been spent
    490 man-weeks have been achieved
    1000 man-weeks is the total departmental estimate
The predicted total expenditure for the department becomes–

$$\left(\frac{500}{490} \times 1000\right) \text{ man-weeks } = 1020 \text{ man-weeks}$$

In more general terms –

$$\frac{\text{actual expenditure } \times \text{ corresponding estimate}}{\text{related achievement}} = \text{predicted spend}$$

Man-weeks were used in the above example rather than the more usual man-hours in order to emphasise the broader approach which engineering design control demands. The inaccuracies which are inherent in estimating for design functions do not really justify expression of any results in man-hours. However, in practice all figures would probably be calculated in man-hours, especially since cost accounting is usually based on these units. It is, nevertheless necessary to bear in mind that any results deriving from calculations in man-hours should be pruned back to exclude all digits or decimal places which the measurement accuracies cannot support.

The actual mechanism of an achievement calculation for an engineering design department is demonstrated in Figure 9.1. Here, another engineering project is presumed to be well under way. The total departmental estimate is seen to be 85 man-weeks, and the analysis reveals that 39·7 man-weeks have been achieved. Against this, expenditure measured at the same date is unfortunately higher, at 49·5 man-weeks. In achieving 46·7 per cent of the work, this department has used up 58·2 per cent of its budget.

Relating Achievement to Expenditure

ACHIEVEMENT ANALYSIS

Department: _Engineering_ Date: March 1968
Project: SERVO CONTROL & SENSOR UNIT Sheet: 1 OF : 1

ACTIVITY		ESTIMATE MAN WEEKS	% ACHIEVED	MAN WEEKS ACHIEVED	MAN WEEKS ACTUAL
0001	System Design	10	100	10	25
0002	Write Design Specification	1	100	1	1
0003	Design + 35 v Power Supply	3	100	3	4
0004	Breadboard Stage	2	100	2	1
0005	Package	2	100	2	1
0006	Prove prototype	1	—	—	—
0007	Write test spec	1	—	—	—
0008	Design + 10 v Power Supply	3	100	3	2
0009	Breadboard stage	2	100	2	1
0010	Package	2	50	1	0·5
0011	Prove prototype	1	—	—	—
0012	Write test spec.	1	—	—	—
0013	Design − 15v Power Supply	3	—	—	—
0014	Breadboard stage	2	—	—	—
0015	Package	2	—	—	—
0016	Prove prototype	1	—	—	—
0017	Write test spec	1	—	—	—
0018	Design sensor circuit	10	100	10	8
0019	Breadboard stage	3	100	3	2
0020	Package	3	40	1·2	1·5
0021	Prove prototype	2			
0022	Write test spec	1			
0023	Design servo control	5	20	1	2
0024	Breadboard stage	4			
0025	Package	2			
0026	Prove prototype	3			
0027	Write test spec	1			
0028	Design main chassis	2	25	0·5	0·5
0029	Carry out system test	2			
0030	Environmental test	2			
0031	Write overall test spec	4			
0032	Write operating instructions	3			
0033					
0034					
0035					
0036					
0037					
0038					
0039					
0040					
	Departmental totals	85	46.7%	39.7	49.5

FIGURE 9.1 TYPICAL DEPARTMENTAL ACHIEVEMENT ANALYSIS
Estimates, progress and costs are compared on this form
in order to predict the probable final expenditure

These results can now be used to predict the final departmental expenditure, assuming that no corrective measures will be taken to improve subsequent performance. On this basis, final expenditure could be expected to reach –

$$\left(\frac{49\cdot5}{39\cdot7} \times 85\right) = 106 \text{ man-weeks}$$

This represents a departmental overspend of 23 man-weeks. If this rate of expenditure were allowed to continue unchecked, not only would profits be eroded away, but the timescale could also suffer. Much can often be done to improve performance, however, and even apparently hopeless situations can be retrieved, if taken in time.

Stricter control of modifications should help to curb unnecessary spending and conserve budgets. Whilst changes requested by the customer can usually be accepted (because they will be paid for) all other requests for modifications must be vetted very carefully, and only those which are really essential to project success should be allowed. Modification control, a very important aspect of project management, will be discussed at greater length in a later chapter.

At project level, objectives are often related to estimates or budgets. Personal performance of individuals, especially in software activities, can be much improved by the setting of achievement goals or objectives. There is no reason why this should not be undertaken as a counter measure against predicted overspending, although it would perhaps have been preferable to set the objectives more firmly at the start of the project. In the face of dwindling budgets, the demands made on individuals from their objectives should be more stringent, but this can only be achieved by first gaining their full co-operation and by making sure that the tasks set are not impossible to perform.

If, in spite of all efforts, a serious overspend still threatens, there remains the possibility of replenishing the project coffers from their original source – the customer. This feat can sometimes be achieved by reopening the fixed-price negotiation whenever a suitable opportunity presents itself. An excuse to negotiate may be provided for example by a major customer modification or as a result of economic factors beyond the contractor's control. Failing this step, smaller modifications or project spares can be priced generously in order to offset the areas of loss or low profitability.

The significant point to bear in mind is that without achievement analysis, forewarning of possible budget excesses may not be received in time to allow any action at all. When such a prediction is made, despair is the wrong philosophy. It is obviously far better to carry out a careful reappraisal of the remaining project activities and to explore all possible avenues which might lead to a restoration of the original project profit targets.

REGULAR ACHIEVEMENT ANALYSIS

If achievement analysis is performed for every department at regular intervals, the first few results could be fairly unreliable owing to the relatively high proportion of work in progress compared to completed activities. After an initial "settling down" period, however, a consistent pattern of prediction should begin to emerge. It is a very good plan to plot a graph of all results in order that any trends may be seen to better advantage. The intervals at which measurements are taken must depend partly upon the nature and overall scale of the project and also on the preference of the individual project manager.

In Figure 9.2 a graph is shown which illustrates one possible pattern of results. This example, still concerned with engineering design, has been plotted from checks made at fortnightly intervals. Although labelled a "typical pattern," wide variations could of course be encountered in practice. Several features of this particular curve are, however, worth noting. The first point plotted, taken at zero project time, is the predicted engineering design expenditure unmodified by experience. In other words, this is the original estimate, and budget, taken straight from the task list.

The next one or two points display rather startling variations, since they are based, in statistical parlance, on a sample which is too small. These early results also contain a very high proportion of assessed progress rather than completed activities. As time proceeds and the tally of completed work begins to mount up it is not very long before a more consistent trend shows, so that after a couple of months the results carry sufficient weight to determine the necessity for corrective action.

At about the sixth week in the example, a fairly consistent overspend condition becomes apparent. Any management, or department, faced with the prospect of overrunning budgets must take

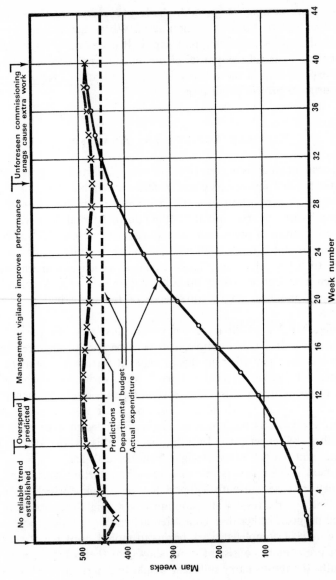

FIGURE 9.2 DEPARTMENTAL ACHIEVEMENT PREDICTIONS
A typical display resulting from a departmental achievement analysis

188

some action, and some degree of success in holding down the rate of expenditure was obviously gained in this case. In fact, the situation is seen to improve steadily up to about week number 30.

In most projects a danger exists that work will not be cut off completely after the last scheduled task has been finished. Clean-up operations, on-site activities, drawing corrections, and commissioning problems are all possible causes of a last minute addition to costs. Sometimes feverish activity takes place during the final phases of a project in order to achieve delivery on time, and this too can give rise to unexpected expenditure. This has obviously happened in the example of Figure 8.2, where there has been a sharp rise in the rate of spending during the last eight weeks or so.

Now compare the graph showing predicted expenditure with that drawn to record actual costs, which is also included on Figure 9.2. The cost curve is cumulative, showing the build up of costs rather than the costs incurred during each period of measurement. Notice how much more information is gleaned from one glance at the predicted curve than can be derived from a study of expenditure, especially during the early part of the project. The overspend danger is simply not shown up at all from the actual cost curve until very late in the project, when any attempt at corrective action would be far too late.

PRODUCTION ACHIEVEMENT

So far, discussion of achievement measurement has been confined to one department only: engineering design. Fairly obviously, the drawing office can be subjected to analysis by the same methods, so that no fresh problems need be expected from that area. At first sight, however, production departments are a very different proposition, being far removed from the abstract world of design and development.

Fortunately, there is no practical reason to prevent these same methods from being extended to cover all production activities. In fact, the process is made easier, since now one is dealing not with theories and subjective assessments, but with the tangible fruits of actual productive labour.

The basis for allocating work values to each production activity again stems from the project task list, together with its associated estimates. By the time the work is actually carried out, however, the production engineers or production planning department may have prepared a work breakdown which is far more detailed than the original task list. This will have been made possible by the availability of production drawings, produced after the task list was compiled. It then becomes necessary to group the detailed processes into sections, each of which is arranged to correspond to one of the tasks originally listed. If this is not done there can be no common ground on which to compare achievement to budget.

When the processes or other detailed production instructions have been grouped to correspond to the original tasks, steps must be taken to arrange that collection of actual cost data also divides out under the same group headings. This is done by paying particular attention to the allocation of cost code numbers. The time booked to every job will be recorded against a number which includes some identifying number, relating the work to the correct task. This argument, and the cost coding methods, will become clearer by reference back to Figure 3.1.

There are many ways in which production activities can be recognised as being complete. These might include acceptance into a "finished goods store," dispatch to the customer, or the signature of an inspection docket. Inspection documents, if routed through a project management department, can provide most of the production progress data which is necessary, provided of course that stage inspection is being carried out. Alternatively, the information can be collected on progress sheets filled out by the various foremen, or by progress chasers.

Work in progress should also be taken into account, especially where the project is large, and contains activities of long duration. This will, of course, entail the collection of progress reports from all production departments at regular intervals. In general, however, these assessments of production achievement will be more accurate than those made for design work, since by the time production is under way there will exist detailed drawings against which progress can be measured.

Production activities may employ a wide range of different labour grades, drawn from several departments. Which of these should be subjected to achievement analysis must depend upon the degree of control considered necessary. It is perhaps an unwise policy to attempt a detailed analysis of every conceivable cost centre. Overambition in this direction, leading to a multiplicity of facts, figures and prediction curves could involve so much effort for little or no return that disillusionment with the whole process of achievement monitoring might set in.

Probably the best course is to analyse the performance of departments rather than individual labour grades. In this way, each departmental manager can be provided with a feedback of his performance against budgets. The vital factor is to ensure that each major cost centre is analysed regularly and given a separate place in the achievement measurements, in order that effective cost versus budget comparisons can be made.

MONITORING BY MILESTONES

Sometimes it is possible to make better use of actual expenditure curves by annotating them or by adding more information. These alternatives, if less effective than full-scale achievement analysis, may appeal to the project manager who lacks the time or facilities necessary to carry out the procedures already described. Two possible avenues of approach can be considered.

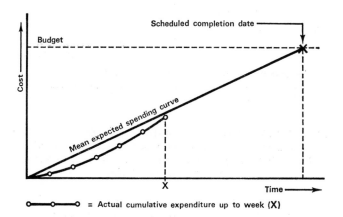

FIGURE 9.3 COSTS COMPARED TO A SIMPLE PREDICTION CURVE
This departmental cost curve shows costs compared to a planned rate of expenditure. The value of this display is somewhat restricted because there is no indication of the corresponding achievement

First, as seen in Figure 9.3, the approximate rate of expenditure can be monitored, and plotted cumulatively against time. At one extreme, if no money is being spent at all, then it is a fair assumption that no progress is being made either. No one would argue with this statement which stands up to any logical investigation quite well. Unfortunately, this method then proceeds to the less acceptable assumption that if expenditure is being incurred at the predicted rate, progress must be "about right." This indeed can only be regarded as a very rough and ready guide and it could lead to some dangerously wrong conclusions. Mention of the scheme is made here, however, as at least one American company has been known to use it.

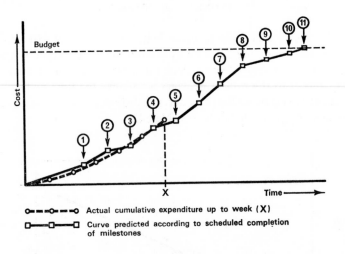

FIGURE 9.4   COSTS COMPARED TO PROJECT MILESTONES
Here the achievement of each milestone can be checked as the costs rise. This affords some measure of cost versus performance monitoring

A variation of the method just described is shown in Figure 9.4, where the predicted rate of expenditure has been calculated and plotted with a good deal more care and attention. This has been done by picking out certain project events which can be considered as significant steps in the road to project completion. Not surprisingly, these particular events are referred to as "milestones." It is important to ensure that the achievement of each milestone can be easily recognised when it happens, either by reporting or by an obvious visual examination of the work.

The curve of predicted expenditure is built up by adding all estimates needed to complete each milestone, taking care to ensure that the grand total is equal to the project total, and no estimates are left out. The expected achievement date for each milestone is then found by reference to the project network diagram or bar chart. A prediction curve for each department can now be drawn by plotting the estimates cumulatively on a graph against time, with each progressive addition to expenditure shown at the expected date for the achievement of its associated milestone.

Monitoring the results then consists of plotting actual expenditure on the same graph and checking whether or not each milestone is in fact achieved on time. If any milestone is not passed on the expected date, the subsequent part of the programme must be rescheduled. When the revised dates for remaining milestones are known, the predicted expenditure curve can be skewed over in the general direction of programme slippage by replotting these late milestones. This ensures that the predicted rate of expenditure is kept in line, broadly speaking, with known achievement. A low rate of actual expenditure, for example, can possibly be shown to correspond with a relatively low rate of progress, in which case only the programme is suffering directly and not the budget. On the other hand, expenditure could be "on plan," but with milestones being achieved too late, indicating that over-spending is taking place.

Disadvantages of the Milestone Method. These are threefold. The information which can be extracted for management use in controlling the project is often obtained after the damage has been done, and certainly much later than the predictions possible with achievement analysis. If programme slippages are going to occur very often, the curves may have to be redrawn frequently, unless some flexible charting method can be devised. Most important of all, the method shows up only qualitative results, indicating trends rather than the more accurate quantitative measurements obtainable from achievement analysis. However, the method involves comparatively little effort and may commend itself to the busy project manager on that basis alone.

Materials Achievement

Material costs have not yet been included in these discussions of achievement analysis. Here, the problem differs from the measurement and consideration of labour costs. If a man is ordered to work on a particular project job, the labour costs are incurred then and there. If he works for ten hours, ten hours will be booked against the appropriate job number and ten hours will appear in the records as the cost of the job.

Material orders, on the other hand, are usually originated well in advance of the time when the actual goods will be received and invoiced. Payment may not follow until several months after the initial order was placed on the supplier. (See Figure 6.4.) There are two ways in which the material costs can be predicted, each resulting in a graph plotted against time. A curve of all material purchases committed can be plotted cumulatively, similar to the example of Figure 6.4. Extrapolation can give some indication of the likely total expenditure which will be reached on project completion. Alternatively, revised material cost estimates can be carried out at regular intervals, using experience on completed tasks as a guide. A graph is then used to display any upward or downward trend which may result.

If a curve of material commitments is to be drawn, care must be taken to include all those other materials which will not be ordered specifically for the project. Any item held in normal production stock, or raw materials from general stock, must be estimated for quantity and cost and added to bring the value committed in terms of purchase orders up to the correct level. The curve will become more useful if milestones can be worked out and shown on the timescale. The budget can then be drawn according to a predicted rate of committed expenditure.

Where it is intended to make regular revisions to the original estimates, based on experience, three elements have to be evaluated. These are –

1 The total value of all purchase orders already placed
2 The estimated value of all purchase orders still not placed (using the task list as a check)
3 The value of materials to be used from general stock

If a graph is plotted, any trend, adverse or otherwise, will be shown up as early as possible.

Whilst it would be quite feasible to record the actual value of materials used up in the completion of each task, the cumulative results might well prove to be misleading. When the final reckoning of project material costs is made, this total cannot be restricted only to those materials which have been usefully employed and lost through scrappage. Any other items which have become surplus, owing possibly to overordering or to design modifications, must be included in the final total. The only possible exceptions to this rule are provided by stock which can be returned to the supplier for full credit, or which can be *profitably* used against a *known* alternative project, for which a firm order exists.

There is often an understandable reluctance to write off materials which are left over as surplus to project requirements. Individuals are sometimes tempted to take these items into general stock in the hope that one day they may eventually be found useful. It is surprising to observe how quickly a storage area can become completely cluttered with such stock in a short space of time. Not only can large volumes of space be consumed in the storage of redundant stock, but the value to be written off eventually can accumulate to embarrassing proportions if it is allowed to mount up unchecked. The day of reckoning has to come and it is better to recognise stock as redundant at the time when it first deserves that description.

Measurement of material achievement on a task basis has another drawback, this time associated with the purchasing policy. Quite obviously, if a project had 100 different activities, each requiring the use of a few screws, the purchasing department would be expected to collate the quantities required and place one single bulk order. If this were not done, no benefits would derive from the supplier's offer of quantity discounts. A similar argument would apply to the purchase of raw materials for widespread project use. The issue of materials from stores against each task could certainly be recorded, but the total material commitment including scrappage and surplus is the result ideally required.

SUBCONTRACT ACHIEVEMENT

The goods and services obtained from subcontractors will almost

195

invariably be ordered against firm price quotations. Each order can be regarded as a separate small contract encompassed within the main contract framework. For all practical purposes these can be considered as material purchases and combined with the material cost records and predictions. Any overspending which does occur in the fulfilment of a subcontract order should fall within the liability of the supplier. Achievement analysis need not, therefore, be extended into subcontracted work other than to check the total commitment of orders placed against budget.

Progress against timescale, and the insistence that suppliers meet their delivery commitments is, of course, a completely different story. The project manager will wish to satisfy himself that every company providing a key supply of materials or services is performing according to plan. This may entail visits to the supplier's premises to certify progress, and inspect his facilities, and can also involve mutual attendance at progress meetings. Generally speaking, however, the question of a supplier's internal costs against achievement will not arise. The only occasions on which costs are likely to be discussed will be if the supplier attempts to justify an increase in the agreed fixed subcontract price, where progress stage payments are involved or where the financial basis and liquidity of the subcontractor gives rise for concern.

The employment of subcontract labour on a main contractor's premises gives rise to a different set of circumstances and conditions. Here it is assumed that any employees provided on a temporary basis by some outside agency would be expected to report to full-time supervisors of the main contractor. Their cost would be seen as a hiring charge, payable to the agency and not as normal wages plus overheads. The work, however, would fall within the control and direction of the main contractor, who must be responsible for the progress and total hiring period. Achievement analysis is therefore necessary, according to the same routines employed for assessing permanent employees' performance.

EFFECT OF MODIFICATIONS ON ACHIEVEMENT

Every modification which is introduced into a project can be expected to have some effect on the level of achievement attained by the departments involved. Before this effect can be considered quantitatively, one significant question must always be answered. Can the customer be held liable for additional costs, or must the work be paid for out of project profits? Control of modifications generally is a subject worthy of separate discussion and Chapter 8 has been devoted to that purpose. It can be assumed, however, that by the time any modification reaches the stage of implementation, approval must have been granted by some specially appointed authority. One duty of this person or committee will be to label each change as "customer funded" or "unfunded," as the case may be.

Taking unfunded modifications first, each must obviously affect the total work load remaining, with no corresponding change to the budgets. In most cases the work load will be increased and the effect will be to depress the real levels of achievement attained in all the affected departments. An appropriate correction to every achievement measurement could be made by adding each modification to the task list, estimating the additional work required. Whilst the total project work estimate would then be increased there could be no corresponding change in the budgets, which henceforth would differ from the original estimates. On the graphs the predicted expenditure curve would take up a new slope but the budget lines could not be redrawn.

In practice, these modifications can be ignored, provided that they are not too numerous and do not significantly cancel work already counted as achieved. Modification costs are often extremely difficult to record, because the work, by its very nature, is intermingled with the original task affected. This is especially true of changes to work which has not been started. If, for instance, a man is engaged in welding up a framework, and a modification was introduced into the drawing before he started, how can he or anyone else record the additional time relevant to that particular modification? Modification costs will show up as an apparent overspend – which is, of course, just what they really are. Achievement predictions will be self-correcting as these overspends are picked up, even if they are not immediately identifiable as being expressly due to modifications.

Unfunded modifications which nullify work already carried out must always be taken into account by erasure of the relevant achievement from the records. This will be done for every department affected, and either whole tasks or parts of them may have to be reinstated into the remaining work load. In this way, the achievement calculations can be kept on a true course. Taking an example, suppose that in the case illustrated by Figure 9.1 there arose a modification which demanded a complete restart of activity 0020 "package design sensor." Achievement for this item would have to revert to zero, which would mean subtracting 1·2 man-weeks from the column total of man-weeks achieved. This would cut the measured departmental achievement back to 38·5 man-weeks. The predicted expenditure for this department on completion of the project would then be calculated at 109 man-weeks, compared to a budget of 85 man-weeks, and a previous prediction of 106 man-weeks.

Funded modifications can be considered as new tasks, for addition to both the task list and the budgets. Estimates are made for the additional work; the appropriate departmental estimates, the project price, and the delivery schedule are also revised. The curves for predicted expenditure will be increased by the appropriate amount, but the budgets can also be raised accordingly.

THE PROJECT LEDGER

A picture has now been built up of a collection of statistics, which can be displayed on graphs to show the predicted and actual performance of each department against budgets. Successful budgetary control and cost prediction therefore requires a certain amount of accurate book-keeping not only within the boundaries of the accounts department, but also in the office of the project manager.

The dossier of achievement returns, estimates, and budgets, all based upon the project task list, can be regarded as a project ledger. The ledger account is credited with the cost of any additional modifications and work achieved is debited, to leave a record of the amount of work outstanding. At any time, it should be possible to consult the ledger to determine the cost/budget status of every department engaged on the project.

Calculating Aids for the Project Ledger: Computers and Bar Charts.
If computer facilities are readily available, it would seem a sensible step to set up the project ledger in the computer store. This approach would have to rely on the existence of a suitable programme, but is particularly attractive where a computer is already employed for networking and resource scheduling. The cumulative effect of delays

in collecting data and converting it to a form suitable for input to the computer must be considered and kept to a minimum. It is no good predicting overspends so late that by the time the print-outs are to hand the money has already been spent.

Computer assisted up-dating of project ledger sheets removes the problem encountered when purely clerical methods are employed. The idea of relying on an automatic, easily changed file in the computer's store is preferable to wrestling with up-dates on written sheets. Repetitive erasures and corrections to pencilled achievement entries on cards can eventually result in a set of very tatty documents with a high error risk.

Projects which have been subjected to manual resource levelling techniques, or which have been displayed on an adjustable bar chart for other reasons, offer an interesting possibility for mechanical achievement analysis. The method extends the use of the bar chart, converting it, in effect, into a physical representation of the project ledger. The procedure has the advantage of simplifying all calculations and displaying the results in a vivid easily understood fashion.

Figure 9.5 shows how a bar chart can be extended to show achievement. The example is taken directly from the garage project discussed in Chapter 5. Here, an addition has been made to the bar chart which was evolved to show the optimum usage of resources within the shortest possible project time. Notice that, compared to the original bar chart shown in Figure 5.6, this chart has been given an extra section labelled "progress ladders." One ladder has been provided for each different cost centre. In this case, only two cost centres have been defined: skilled and unskilled labour.

Each progress ladder has been constructed by adding up the total amount of strip used for each department or cost centre. This may differ slightly from the actual estimate, because the degree of resolution of a wall chart is restricted by the scale, in this case not really being divisible into periods of less than one day. The errors so introduced should not be significant and often tend to cancel each other out. A scale has been provided alongside each ladder, enabling the height at any point to be read off with facility. It is seen that the total height of the skilled section is thirty-two man-days, and that of the labourer section is twenty-nine days. In practice these ladders would be marked out by narrow adhesive tape, or paint.

Now refer to Figure 9.6. Here it is assumed that the garage project has been in progress for some days, and the actual date reached is

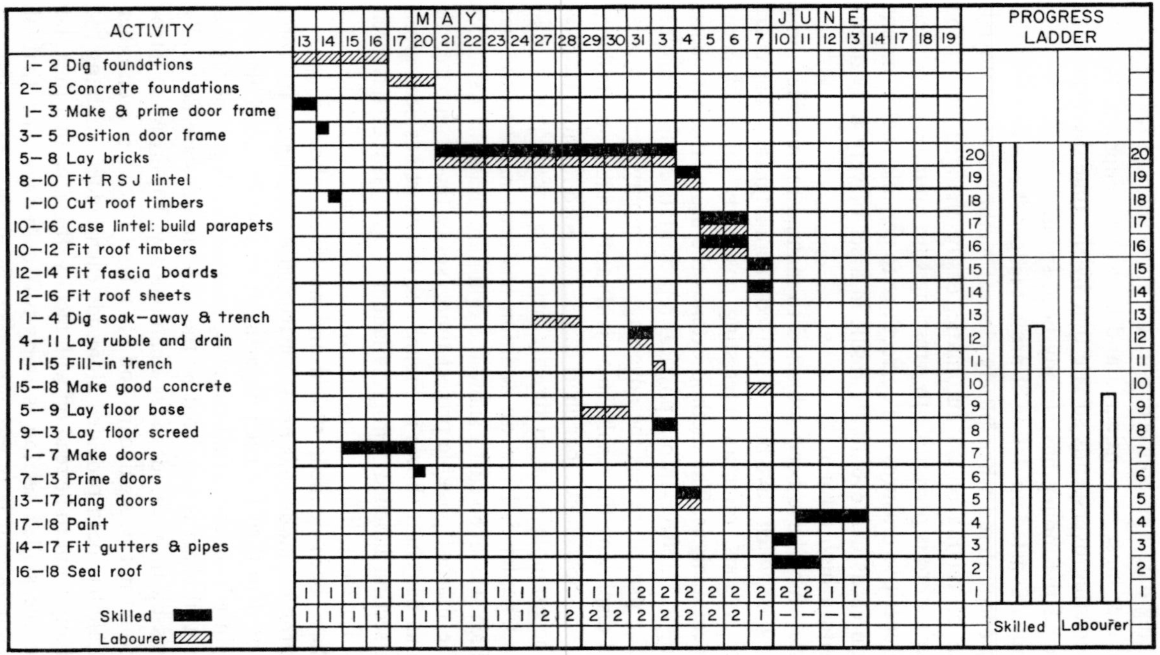

FIGURE 9.5 PROGRESS LADDERS

The garage project schedule has been extended by the addition of "progress ladders" which allow departmental achievements to be computed mechanically

200

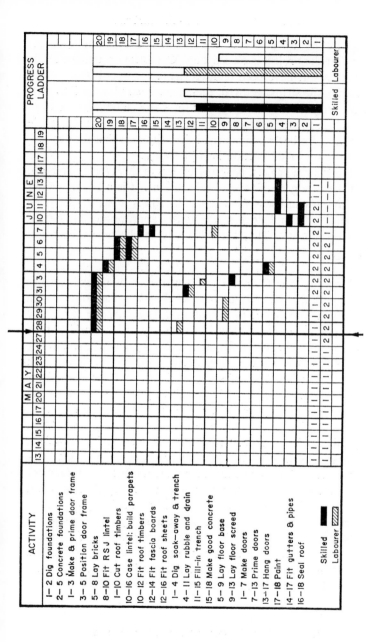

FIGURE 9.6 PROGRESS LADDERS IN ACTION

The garage project is shown here "on schedule" at day 28. The progress ladders have scales which allow achievement to be read off indicated by the movable date-line cursor. It is apparent from the diagram that the project is on schedule. Completed activities, to the left of the cursor, have been removed from the board. But instead of discarding the strips removed, these have been plugged into their respective progress ladders. Note that the skilled labour has reached eleven weeks, so that the percentage completion for this labour grade has reached $(\frac{11}{32} \times 100)\%$. Similarly, it is easily seen that the achievement for the unskilled portion is $(\frac{12}{29} \times 100)\%$.

On a fairly large project, progress ladders of this type can remove much of the drudgery of routine calculations. It is a simple matter to plug in extra tasks as funded modifications arise, at the same time extending each ladder scale by the appropriate amount to maintain equilibrium. Thus the bar chart has become the project ledger.

Disadvantages of Bar Charts. There are one or two disadvantages associated with the use of adjustable bar charts in place of a written project ledger. The degree of resolution afforded by the chart may not allow accuracies closer than one man-day to be considered, or even one man-week. This resolution accuracy will depend solely upon the scale to which the chart can be constructed, this in turn depending on the amount of space available and the size of the adjustable board. A project lasting for three years, for example, and divided up into weekly periods, would require a board at least 1 metre long, with more space necessary for the progress ladders. Usually this particular type of inaccuracy is not a serious problem.

A more serious problem arises whenever errors are made in setting up the progress ladders or when changes are made to the total work content as a result of customer modifications. Every time the chart is updated the situation which it indicated immediately before the alteration is irrevocably erased. It is not a bad plan, therefore, to supplement the mechanical aid with a written account, although there will be no need to go through the tedious procedure of actual written calculations of achievement. Alternatively, colour photographs could be taken of the chart at regular intervals.

PREDICTING PROJECT PROFITABILITY

Once a basis has been established for the collection of achievement analysis statistics from all departments, it is a logical and progressive step to put all these results together into a composite prediction of total project costs. Of course, the first prediction of total costs is that made when the tender is prepared against initial estimates and when the progress is zero. Subsequent achievement analysis and cost predictions are a means of checking performance against these estimates in order that any adverse factors will be shown up at the earliest possible time.

As in the case for departmental performance, the total cost predictions can be plotted on a graph against project time, so that any upward or downward trends can be clearly seen. When the work is completed, the final costs will be known and an investigation can be conducted to compare actual expenditure with estimates. The results of such an investigation have value in influencing the estimates to be applied to all similar future projects. Post-mortems of this type, however, have little relevance to the control of an existing project. Only by keeping a constant check on the dynamic state of the activity project can information be derived in time to allow the application of any necessary action to correct possible overspends.

Before the predictions from all the various departments can be added together and combined with the predicted material expenditure, they must be brought to one common denominator. Quite obviously, this entails conversion from man-time into money, using the appropriate standard rates according to the types of labour employed. Conversion for each department must be carried out before the results can be added together, since the man-time results previously calculated will all carry different cost values per man-hour, owing to variations in the skills employed. This does not mean, however, that time and effort were wasted in working in man-hours previously. For any given grade of labour or manufacturing operation, units of man-time are the only fundamental basis for measurement, because they are not affected by inflation or rising costs. Records of man-time provide the only reliable yardsticks against which experience can be built up for estimating future projects.

Cost monitoring and prediction is usually aimed at protecting the eventual profitability. Accordingly, the final prediction graphs for any project should show both cost and budget levels, together with the effective net selling price. Both the targeted and predicted gross profit margins will be displayed, so that as time proceeds a wary eye can be kept on the likely outcome. Notice that the budget and

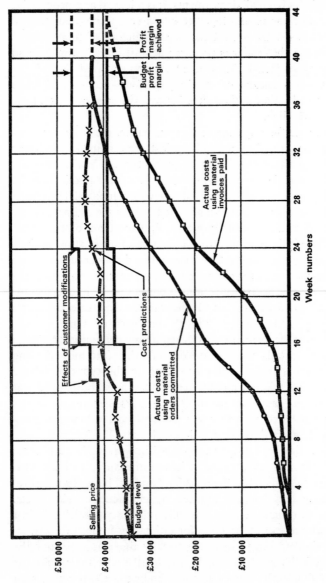

FIGURE 9.7 A COST/PROFIT PROJECT PREDICTION GRAPH

A curve of this type is the reward gained by carrying out detailed achievement analysis. It enables management to be given an early warning of any possible threat to project profits from overspending of budgets. Try placing a piece of card over the entire curve, and then move it in stages from left to right. Notice how, as each week is uncovered, the predicted cost curve yields information which is far more significant than that provided by the simple cost accumulation graphs below it price levels will have to be readjusted whenever a customer modification is introduced which affects the contract price.

Figure 9.7 shows one type of curve which could result from the regular plotting of cost predictions for the whole project. In this particular example the project is shown at the completed stage. It is possible to recapture some of the sense of occasion which would have existed during the active stages of the project by placing a piece of card over the diagram and moving it from left to right in fortnightly steps.

Curves of this type will prove to be an invaluable aid to the project manager because they serve to reinforce the presentation of facts to higher management. The existence of a set of departmental graphs, and one which shows the total cost/profit status of the project, saves much time at review meetings, enabling the project manager to dispense with the recitation of a tedious set of figures. A table of figures usually only indicates the status stage of a project at the time of measurement, but the presentation of graphs can display dynamic trends, from which managers can deduce all they need to make any necessary decisions to keep the project on the right track.

INDEX

ABC PRODUCTION priorities 148
ABC system of stock control
124–7
Achievement
analysis 180–7
design 182–7
effect of modifications 196–8
materials 194–5
production 189–91
subcontract 195–6
Activities
identification 53
interdependence 54
Activity lists 142–4
Authority of the project manager
12
Arrow diagrams 52–3

BAR charts 22, 77, 198–202
proprietary kits 52, 90
Breakdown of work
for estimating purposes 24
Bridging contracts 44
British Standards Specifications
for material purchases 120
for raw materials 138
Budgets 20, 21, 42, 141, 180, 198
Build schedules 168–72

CALCULATING aids for the project
ledger 198–202
Card index
for stock collation 103–5
Catalogues, limitations as purchase
specifications 120

Change committee 21
Clerical routines for materials stor-
age 139
Committed materials expenditure,
as an early warning system
135
Common parts—see stock collation
Computer 62, 90–1, 113, 199
Concessions 172–8
Contingencies 41, 44, 69
Contract purchasing—see Project
purchasing
Contractor's specification 15–17
Contractual commitments 14–15
Correction factors applied to
estimators 40
Cost of capital employed 179
Cost of modifications 156–60
Cost-plus contracts 45
Costing 180
material cost collection methods
133–7
Coverite project 164–8
CPA (Critical Path Analysis)
52–62
CPM—see CPA
Crash costs 59
Critical path, calculation of 56
Critical path network 23, 46
Customer's requirements 14
Customer specification 14–15

DECENTRALISING the estimating
function 35
Design achievement analysis
182–7

Development programmes 17
Draughtsmen as optimistic estimators 39–40
Dummies as an aid to network clarity 67

ECONOMIC purchase quantities 129
Emergency modifications 164–8
Empire builders 40
Engineering query notes 175–6
Engineers as optimistic estimators 39–40
Engineers, their role in supporting the estimators 33
Escalation 42
Estimates, collection methods 34–7
Estimating
  accuracy 37, 46–7
  capabilities of individuals 36
  cost of estimating 33
  errors 39–42, 46–7
  for materials 31–8
  for production 16–17, 30–8
  forms 27–30
  helping production staff 37
  interpretation and correction 38, 41
  levels 25–6
  modification costs 156–9
  network durations 69
  time available for preparation 33
  without drawings 32–4
Estimators
  inconsistent 41
  optimistic 39
  pessimistic 40
  seniority 33
Events, identification 53
Exception reporting 153
Expected time (PERT) 62
Expediting of purchase orders 130–2
Experience of previous projects related to estimating 33, 37

FAMILY tree 23, 96, 103, 106–8
Feedback 144
Filing cabinet project 94–113
Fixing the price—*see* Pricing
Float 55
  free 89–90
  independent 90
  total 85, 88–9

GANTRY project 56–62
Gantt charts—*see* Bar charts
Garage project 76–90
Goods inwards inspection 119
Government contracts 27, 43, 173
Graphs to show dynamic project trends 205

HASTE versus accuracy 152
Honeywell Controls Ltd, operating theatre projects 68, 71–5

ICSL computing services 91
Immediate action orders 148–52
Independent float—*see* Float
Inspection reports 177–8
Inventory turn ration 125, 129
Invoices, clearance of suppliers' 135
Irregular stores withdrawals 138

KITTING 96, 139
Kosy-Kwik case study 164–8

LADDER activities 145
Ladder networks 65
Letters—value of the written word in expediting purchase orders 131
Line of balance 105–14
Loss-incurring projects 47

MANAGEMENT by exception 62, 114, 140, 153
Management supports 11–13
Marked-up prints 167
Market conditions 44
Master record index 171
Materials
  achievement analysis 194–5
  call-off orders 122–3
  choice of supplier 118
  commitments 194
  expediting 130–2
  lead times 30, 115
  overheads 30
  proportion of total project costs 37, 116
  security 138
  shortages 115, 132, 139–40
Measurement of achievement for invoicing purposes 179
Milestones 191–3
Minutes of progress meetings 148
Modifications
  authorisation 160, 164
  classification as essential or desirable 163
  committee 160–4
  control 21
  costs 42
  emergency 164–8
  labels 171–2
  liability 155–6, 160–1, 197
  origins 155–6
Most likely time (PERT) 62
Multi-project scheduling 149

NETWORK analysis as a management tool 70
Network analysis session as a forum for collecting estimates 36
Network sessions 68–9, 141
Networks' inability to show resource requirements 76

OBJECTIVES of project management 10

Optimistic time (PERT) 62
Ordering to a plan 122
Overheads 29
  under-recovery 158

PART collation 103–5
Part-numbers of non-interchangeable parts 169
Penalty clauses 116
PERT (Programme Evaluation and Review Technique) 62–3
Pessimistic time (PERT) 62
Planning
  importance of 48
  notation for 48
Pre-allocation of stocks 133, 138
Pricing 16, 30, 43–5
  responsibility for 45
  spare parts 29
Product specification 17–22
Production achievement analysis 189–91
Production costs' dependence on design specification 15–16
Production estimates
  with drawings 30–2
  without drawings 32–4
Production priorities 148–52
Profitability 115–16, 202–5
Progress ladders 199–202
Progress meetings 146–8
Progress payments 179
Progress reporting 144–6
  for management 153–4
  related to cost plus projects 45
  to customer 154
Project estimating compared to production estimating 24–5
Project ledger 198–202
Project management teams 25
Project manager, personal qualities 10
Project purchasing 132–7
Purchase specifications 120
Purchasing cycle 117–20
Purchasing department responsibilities 38, 117

Purchasing
  small quantities 127–8
  stock or project 132–7
  see also Materials

QUALITY control, relevance of concessions 178
Quantity discounts for purchased materials 128
Quotations
  cost of preparation 33
  preparation 15, 33

RECORD player case study 17–22
Resource scheduling 51, 76–93
Return on investment 21
Risk decisions associated with design haste 153
  see also contingencies

SALES forecasts 21
Scheduling
  by computer 90–1
  cost of 91
  material deliveries 122–4
  multi-project 149
  parts 105–14
  resources 51, 76–93
Seniority of estimator 33
Serial numbering of units 168–70
Shortage lists 139
Space problems in materials storage 137
Specification
  contractor's 15–17
  customer's 14–15
  product 17–22
  purchase 120–2

Stage payments—*see* progress payments
Standard estimating tables 32
Standard networks 67–8
Stock collation 103–5
Stock control 96, 124–7, 139
  ABC system 124–7
  max/min levels 105, 127, 133
  two bin method 127
Stock identification 138
Stock storage 137–40
Subcontractors 2, 149, 152
  achievement measurement 195–6
Support for the project manager 11–13, 70
Surplus stocks 128, 136

TASK code numbers 25
Task, definition of a 24
Task lists 24–7
Technical cost investigations 27
Tender—*see* Quotations
Time available and required 48
Timescale/budget relationship 20
Tooling costs 29
Total float—*see* Float
Training in network analysis 70
Training of customer technicians 24
Training of the project manager 10, 12
Tree project 54
Two bin method of stock control 127

UNWORKABLE schedules 91–3